Find Your Strong

FIND YOUR STRONG

Learn to Ditch the Excuses!

by
Natalie Heckert

Find Your Strong: Learn to Ditch the Excuses!

Copyright © 2023 by Natalie Heckert

ISBN 979-8-9878904-0-0 (Paperback)
ISBN 979-8-9878904-8-6 (Hardcover)

SELF-HELP / Wellness / Weight Loss

Cover Design: Achieve Systems Graphics
Cover Photograph: Princeton Clark
Interior Design: Jeff Scott Ruiz
Copyright owned by Natalie Heckert.

Printed in the United States of America.

Dedication

This book is dedicated to all of my past, current and future clients. Their struggles, excuses and eventual successes were the catalyst for me to write this book. Throughout my career, my clients have given me the opportunity to serve them. They have inspired me to build my business and invent the *Club E Fit Platform System*. Without their continued love and support, I may have not pushed myself to achieve my career goal of helping others Find the Strong in themselves.

If you want to live happier, healthier, leaner and stronger, you have to be willing to change the way you approach your current health journey. It is easy to make and hide behind your excuses. It takes hard work, the support of others, the will to change, and the mindset that you can do it.

I know you can do this. Let's get to work!

—Natalie

Table of Contents

Preface

Natalie Heckert is a high-energy presenter and personal trainer who specializes in working with individuals, groups and corporations to inspire fitness and weight loss that can be realistically incorporated into everyday life.

She has a four-year college degree in Community Health/Sports Science and is a certified trainer and group fitness instructor.

Natalie has also worked as an aerobics instructor, personal trainer and motivational speaker in the Los Angeles, California area, and has trained and taught with some of the best fitness instructors in the world.

She is the CEO of NATS (Nutrition & Aerobic Training Service) and the inventor of the *E Fit Platform System*, and has presented at national and international fitness expos as a fitness expert and motivational speaker.

She created and aired an "As Seen on TV" 30-minute infomercial and DVD training series.

Natalie created an E Fit Master Trainer program and a national CEC-approved manual so trainers could have the ability to train anybody, anytime and anywhere while earning money and training clients with the *E Fit Platform System*.

She designed, developed and implemented a corporate state-of-the-art wellness center, and has trained with select Army and Air Force bases using the *E Fit Platform System*.

She originated and developed a two-year Health & Fitness Specialist Degree program in partnership with a Community Technical College while serving as an adjunct teacher.

Natalie has served on the Board of Directors for the National Exercise Trainers Association (NETA) Certification Board.

She has been a television and radio guest, most notably on ABC, NBC and CBS; and was also a Mrs. Minnesota finalist, a contestant on *The Price is Right*, an auditioner for Oprah's *Next Best Invention*, and trainer for a contestant on NBC's *The Biggest Loser*.

She has also employed handicapped adults to assist with her product line assembly.

Acknowledgments

Several years ago, I began meeting with Juliet Ray Brambrink. With her help, we created the first draft of this book. She put my thoughts into words and started me on this journey of achieving one of my life goals of being a published author.

I would like to thank my husband, who read and edited the book through its various stages. He encouraged me to finish what I started many years earlier. Without his help, this book might still be sitting in my computer storage files.

All of the excuses in this book were provide to me by my clients. They trusted me and sought me out to help them create a better version of themselves. They listened to my advice, actively incorporated what I suggested, and found and shared their successes with me. Thanks for trusting me and giving me the opportunity to serve you! It is my hope that your success and the lessons we learned together will inspire others to BUST their own excuses and Find the Strong in themselves.

I would like to thank everyone who helped me invent,

manufacture and market my *Club E Fit Platform System*. The E Fit has given me another tool to help others take charge of their own health journey. It has allowed me to help a wide variety of clients take control of their personal fitness—from those who could not get out of bed to those who were professional athletes. The E Fit system and all those who have supported me opened doors to meet others and gain experiences I may have otherwise not had the opportunity to meet.

Last but not least, thanks to all my friends and family who have supported and encouraged me throughout my career. Your thoughtful comments, cards, emails and other mementos have continued to push me to always do and be my best. You have given me the courage to show others that they have the power to change their lives, and you have inspired me to write this book with the hope of inspiring others to Find the Strong inside of them.

Introduction

Let's Bust Your Excuses!

I have written this book in an easy-to-read, common-sense format. It is not filled with data, scientific research or fancy, hard to understand words. Why? Because everything you will read in this book came from clients I have served. It is a compilation of their excuses and what I shared with them to BUST those excuses!

I have heard many excuses over the past 30 years working with my clients. There were a variety of reasons they gave. Some did it to protect themselves and their self-esteem. Others may have tried to reduce their feelings of being overwhelmed, to avoid feeling guilty or to hide the fact that they weren't really motivated to accomplish goals they talked about achieving. Some were afraid they might fail. Others were unsure if they possessed the talents and skills they needed to contribute to their own growth and progress or of those around them.

At times, my clients used excuses when they were unable

to face the truth or admit the true reason for their emotions or behaviors. They also used excuses to defend their behaviors or delay taking action when it was needed. Others made excuses as a means of shirking their responsibility. Many faced internal challenges, so they would place blame on external conditions to avoid facing that reality.

Making excuses caused them to sell themselves short when it came to their abilities and how they performed in certain situations. It was an avoidance behavior that prevented them from getting what they desired or needed to accomplish. The truth is that every excuse took them further away from reaching their full potential.

Their excuses may have stopped them from taking advantage of opportunities they might never get back. They could have slowed their growth and hindered success in areas they could otherwise have been thriving in.

As you read through these pages, I encourage you to reflect on each situation and ask yourself how it may relate to something you have faced in your life or may be challenged with right now.

I hope I can motivate you to improve your life, health, eating, exercise and service habits by using the advice I share in these pages. I want you to live HAPPIER, HEALTHIER and STRONGER after reading this book.

—Natalie

Nutrition and *Stop* Dieting

When you drop the excuses…

Food is huge in our society. It's the focal point of most social gatherings. Memories and feelings are associated with it. Some people have problems with too much food and others have trouble with not enough. Either way, many people don't get the right foods their bodies need to be healthy. In my years of personal training, I've found that it's hard for people to change their eating habits. They don't know what change actually means or they don't want to do the work that's required to change.

I've found that the only way to effectively get healthier in the long term is to eat a healthy diet 80-90% of the time while incorporating a fitness plan into our daily routine. That's it! Ask anyone who has lost weight and kept it off. They've done it by moving their bodies more and following a healthy diet.

Diet is a scary word. The word "die" is in there! What holds most people up is that they don't want to diet. They don't want to give up the foods they love. They don't want to eat foods they don't like, that taste different or require effort to prepare. People have a ton of excuses for not eating right.

Many people don't have solid *reasons* for not eating healthy; they have *excuses*. What's the difference between those two words? A reason is something you honestly can't get past. An excuse is something you can't easily get past, so you find reasons not to do it. Most people have excuses instead of reasons. That stops them from eating healthier and exercising.

You may think you don't make excuses. You may think you're the exception and that there are legitimate reasons why you don't eat healthy foods. Perhaps that's true. I would ask you, "Why aren't you eating healthier?"

I challenge you to turn the pages and find out if you relate to any of the reasons my clients have tried to use with me for not taking better care of themselves. Read how I let them know that an excuse is just a reason not to try. If you do have a great reason for not eating healthy, then congratulations! Continue to eat the way you have been, but don't expect your body to get leaner and healthier, and don't expect to feel healthier and stronger.

"My diet starts Monday. I'm going to start on Monday."

Why is Monday special? There's nothing you can do on a Monday (or New Year's Day, after a vacation, or whenever) that you can't do today. If a diet is supposed to start on a Monday, it's probably not going to start at all. *I'll start Monday after lunch. Monday is my last day of not dieting.* Pretty soon, Monday is over. Then, the excuses will start for why you're still not eating right.

Monday is a slightly better-sounding way of saying you aren't going to start at all. It's a way of procrastinating and putting off something hard. Procrastinating doesn't make anything easier; it just makes it easier to avoid. Starting on Monday sounds great; but if you started right away, you could have the benefit of a few extra days of healthy eating instead of a binging period beforehand. You could make things easier on yourself by starting right away instead of psyching yourself out over a magical start date.

Monday dieting is hard. Thinking about dieting on Monday could cause you a lot of stress, so start eating healthier today. It may be hard, but I guarantee it's a lot easier on your mind and body than suddenly cutting out your favorite foods on Monday.

Start now. Go easy on yourself. You don't have to start out perfectly. Maybe today you remove one can of soda. Tomorrow, you replace your usual afternoon snack with fresh vegetables. The next day, drink eight glasses of water instead of a soda or other sugary drink. By the time Monday comes around, it won't be a big deal because you'll have already started.

Watch what you say when you start telling people about your new lifestyle. Don't say you started *dieting*. Phrase it positively by saying you started *eating healthy and exercising*. With small and gradual changes, your body will adjust to the new food and you won't freak out at the thought of eating rice cakes instead of chocolate cakes. If you eat junk food all day Sunday in preparation for Monday, you'll hit Monday with more cravings, hunger and fatigue.

This is definitely not the way to start a new lifestyle. Start today and start small. You'll be glad you did. Tomorrow, make another small change. Keep up this routine, and when the next Monday rolls around, eating healthy will almost be a way of life and you'll be on your way to a healthier body!

"I deserve a treat."

You do deserve a treat! You're starting a new lifestyle. You are working hard. You deserve to treat yourself. Treats are important. You won't stick with any eating plan that removes everything you love. You won't stick with any plan when you're thinking about white bread while eating lettuce-wrapped burgers. You won't have any success with a plan where opportunities for sabotage are everywhere. However, you can have success with an eating plan that lets you balance what your body needs with what you want. So have a treat. It's okay.

Many so-called diet plans will tell you not to have treats and to replace "bad" foods with only healthy foods to lose weight. You will lose weight with this plan. You will also feel deprived, and you may not stick with a plan that makes you give up so much; especially when you're surrounded by people who aren't on the same strict diet. So, have a treat! Just balance it into your daily eating plan.

It's much more enjoyable when you can feel good about eating a treat instead of feeling guilty. The trick to treats is moderation. Have a cookie, but not 10. Plan what you are going to eat the rest of the day around your treat. Plan to cut out something you don't like quite as much so you can have your treat and not feel guilty about it. Nothing makes food taste worse than guilt.

Build your daily eating plan to allow yourself a cookie, a piece of birthday cake, a scoop of mashed potatoes and gravy, or whatever else you consider a treat. It's good for your spirit. If you work it into your plan, it shouldn't be bad for your body and you won't feel deprived.

Notice I said *or*. Have a cookie *or* a piece of cake *or* whatever it is you like as a treat. Not a cookie *and* a piece of cake *and* a huge pile of potatoes drowning in gravy. Enjoy your treats and make them count. Don't feel guilty about indulging yourself as part of your healthy lifestyle. Taste your treats and work them into your day by making healthy choices the rest of the day. You won't wreck your figure with one cookie. You will wreck your figure with 10. Have one and enjoy it, then stop.

I always tell my clients, "You cannot burn off in a day what you can eat in just a couple of minutes." It is just too easy to consume a huge amount of calories by eating the wrong foods. Case in point: my husband loves M&Ms. I remind him that he would have to walk a football field from goal post to goal post and back to burn off just one M&M. Think about how many more trips he'd need for the whole bag!

The difference between a healthy eating plan and a diet is that diets only allow you to eat certain foods. Diets usually require you to give up something (fat, calories, carbs, etc.) while allowing you to eat only foods that fit within that diet. Healthy eating means nourishing your body with quality foods. Healthy eating means that as long as you eat plenty of quality fruits and vegetables, whole grains and lean proteins, you can still have the occasional treat. I am all about being allowed to have an occasional treat!

"Reward myself for every goal? Seriously?"

Yes! It's important to reward yourself. Your reward must be something you want and it must be something that aligns with the goal you are working to achieve.

Maybe you're thinking, "Isn't the satisfaction of setting my goal enough? Why do I need to bribe myself with things to work hard?" It would be nice if that wasn't the way things worked, but it's not. Think about it this way: Why do you go to work? You go to work to get a paycheck. That's your reward. Going to work allows you to buy what you need in life. You can save for retirement and will eventually get more opportunities for travel or other things in your life

Rewards are why stores offer discounts when you buy more than one item. Setting goals is no different. If you work hard, you should reward yourself for doing something tangible. You'll get the satisfaction of a job well done. If your goal is to improve something in your life, you'll eventually see the improvement. The reward will be the result of setting your goal, working toward it and achieving success. Who doesn't want to do things that produce great results?

Rewards are especially important if you set a process goal. If your goal is to do something every day (or stop doing something), a reward would be the prize when you eventually meet the goal. Your process goal produces results that are incremental and hard to see at times. You'll need the promise of a reward at the end to keep you moving forward. That might be what you need to keep you excited and driving forward.

At times, setting and achieving goals can be hard. Sometimes, if things aren't working out the way you want them to, simply thinking about the reward might be enough to keep you working toward the goal. Remember, there's nothing wrong with treating yourself for success. Stick with it, work hard and treat yourself!

"I'll work it off later."

A common theory is that if you splurge or binge, you can work out and burn off the extra calories. This is not entirely accurate. It is technically true, but just about impossible. Eating 100 calories can take a few seconds. Working off 100 calories can take an hour of vigorous exercise. Chowing down for five minutes could equate to five hours of working out. Most people don't have that kind of time to exercise or even want to, for that matter.

Working out does burn calories and can help you feel better after a big meal. Working out is important and is an important *part* of a healthy life. Working out is not a cure for overeating.

While it's entirely possible to burn off a splurge item and an additional 500 calories, it's hard if you want to lose one pound a week (a reasonable, healthy goal). You will dread having to burn off 500 calories *more* than you eat because of your decision to splurge. Don't do that to yourself. Eat a balanced diet with an occasional treat and get some form of activity every day.

The flip side of this theory is that eating healthy all day and not working out is a good way to lose weight. Yes, it's great to eat healthy. Yes, some days a long workout won't fit into the schedule. However, doing one without the other is the same as giving yourself half the benefits of a healthy life. You should eat healthy every day *and* get some form of vigorous fitness. That way, you can enjoy an occasional treat or skip an occasional workout without wrecking your healthy body and sabotaging your wellness plan.

Watch out for what I call the "candy bar" diet! This diet tells you to take a pill and eat whatever you want. If it seems easy, it's probably too good to be true. You don't want to spend your day obsessing over calories, whether it's how much you've eaten or how much you've burned off. Don't obsess. Make good choices and plan your day to include quality foods and quality exercise.

You can have that treat but remember you cannot burn off in an hour what you can in a few minutes. Just work it into your day. Really, it's okay.

"Why stop now? I've already blown my diet today."

Everyone messes up. Everyone slips off their plan and eats something unhealthy. Making a life change is hard work and eating healthy is a life change. Don't make it harder by constantly punishing yourself.

It's harder to mess up if you start living a lifestyle instead of going on a diet. If you allow for treating yourself occasionally and if you aren't obsessed with counting calories, fat grams or carbs, it's easier to stick with your plan. On the other hand, you may experience a celebration or a day where you make some not-so-healthy choices. You may even make bad choices. For many people, one little slip can cause them to completely disengage with their healthy lifestyle plan, then they drop their routine because it seems too hard.

Don't be one of those people. Tell yourself, "You've made a lot of good choices. Celebrate those and move past the slip-up." Say this out loud: "NOT TODAY, DEVIL!" He is always there pushing you to screw up and encouraging you to quit. Tell him to shove off and then get back to your plan. YOU CAN DO IT!

One slip-up doesn't mean the whole day will be a downward slide. One off-track day doesn't have to mean it's a bad week. Acknowledge your decision to deviate from your plan, forgive yourself and get right back on track. Eating healthy is a mental game. If you're convinced you can't stick with your plan, you probably won't. HE will be right there to encourage your failure.

A healthy body should be a long-term goal. This means that if you keep your eye on the long-term picture you'll see long-term results. It also means that one missed workout or one not-so-healthy meal won't hurt you in the long run.

Remember that blowing it once in a while won't hurt your diet, but blowing it repeatedly can be devastating. For that matter, one day won't make or break your healthy lifestyle plan or anything else. Repeat this to yourself: "I forgive myself for slipping and I'll do better next time." Think about your goals and the progress you've made to this point. That is what should motivate you to keep up your plan for caring for yourself!

"It's just a cup of coffee."

I hear this a lot. People often don't realize that what they eat or drink affects their health. While no foods should be considered forbidden, there are some that definitely should not be part of an everyday healthy eating plan.

The best way to see what you're really eating and drinking is to keep a food journal. Write down everything you eat or drink. Write down what you put in your body any time you put something in your mouth. Be honest! If you have a huge cup of coffee with cream, flavoring and whipped cream, don't just write down "coffee". At the end of each week, go over your chart and flag any areas for improvement. Also, it's great to have someone else review your chart such as a trainer, nutritionist or a doctor.

As you review your journal, find your trouble areas and make a plan to address them. For example: eat less of a particular food or add more exercise to burn off the additional intake.

While there's nothing you need to totally give up, there are things you can substitute or enjoy less often or in smaller quantities. It could be fancy coffee, a scoop of ice cream after dinner or your mid-afternoon sugar fix.

If you don't drink coffee, substitute the words ice cream, midnight snack or beer—whatever your trouble area is—for the word "coffee". The food or beverage may be different, but the problem and the solution are the same.

My point is that if you love coffee, there's nothing wrong with having it. A cup of coffee is fine. What's less fine are those coffee drinks which are like liquid candy bars. Adding cream, flavor shots and super-sizing it does not make it *just* a cup of coffee. Look at the nutrition charts (which might be hidden) at the coffee shops or look at the nutrition information on the package. Huge latte or-whatever drinks can have more calories, fat grams and sugar than you realize.

While I've already mentioned that counting calories is not the way to a healthy life, they're still what converts to fat in your body and shouldn't be ignored. If you want fancy coffee, make it a treat, but not a routine. Think about what you are drinking, take time to enjoy it and work it into your daily plan. Then, drink plain water the rest of the day. Always be careful what you put into your body. Not all coffees (or bagels or granola bars or…) are the same.

I also mentioned you should enjoy a treat. Just be conscious of what your treat is and how often you treat yourself. If you have one at the beginning of the day, be aware the rest of the day. Your treat may be in the form of a drink or small indulgence, but it doesn't mean it won't count.

"The label says it's Diet."

This is an easy trap to fall into. Diet soda, fat-free cookies and even calorie-free snacks all contain calories that you take into your body. They may fill you up, but won't provide the nutrients your body needs to be healthy. Unless you can work a so-called diet food into your healthy eating plan, there's really no advantage to having them.

Labeling something "diet" doesn't make it healthy. Fill your body with good healthy food. If you don't like fat-free cookies as much as regular cookies, don't eat them. Eat healthy food most of the time, then have a regular cookie as a treat on occasion. You'll feel more satisfied from one regular cookie you love than from 10 fat-free cookies you don't really like.

Ever wonder why fat-free cookies seem to disappear so fast? It's usually because they aren't as satisfying as a few regular cookies, so more get eaten to fill the void. If you're going to have a cookie, pick one you really like and enjoy it. Stop with one, then go about your day without feeling guilty.

I am amazed at how misleading the labels are on our food packaging. My clients tell me they are reading those labels and discovering foods that are healthier. Many times, I have them bring the box or container with them when they come to train with me. After a quick review, I show them how food manufacturers can play games with labels to make you think you are eating healthier.

It doesn't help that FDA guidelines allow companies to be vague with descriptions when it comes to labeling fats and other unhealthy content in products we eat. To add to the labeling confusion, companies usually print this information in small type and write with such scientific complexity you will likely not be able to figure out what's really in the product. Because of this, many people give up on reading labels.

Let's face it—companies make less nutritional foods cheaper and more readily available than healthier options. Go to a public event and notice what kinds of food are being served. They are typically full of fat and made with creams, sauces and other unhealthy ingredients. Go to a professional sporting event and look for a fresh vegetable vendor. In all likelihood, you will not find one. It really shows when you look at the gathering food crowd. I would guess that two thirds of the people standing in line are not in healthy shape.

The important thing about eating healthy is to make sure you truly enjoy the foods you eat. If fat-free cheese won't make you feel as satisfied as regular cheese, find a way to work regular cheese into your day. Don't settle for four pieces of fat-free cheese when you will be happier with one piece of regular cheese.

There are classes available to teach you how to read labels. Attend one and learn so you can truly eat healthier. Remember, it is your responsibility to take care of yourself. Don't depend on others to take care of you. Take your own natural healthy food options to your events. Eat in moderation and exercise so you won't have to worry so much about labels on the food containers.

"But, I need a snack!"

Snacking itself isn't bad for you. Snacking can be a great way to keep yourself from overeating at the next meal. Snacks can help you even out your daily eating plan by giving you the vitamins and nutrients you may not get during regular meals. The secret is to snack smartly. Don't automatically hit the candy machine every afternoon at 2:00. Grab a handful of healthy nuts if you want to pump up your protein. Eat some fresh fruit to get some vitamins. Try low-fat yogurt to get some extra calcium. If it's a while before your next meal, have a snack so you don't overindulge at meal time.

The secret to snacking is to not go overboard. Don't sit at work and munch on buttery microwave popcorn all afternoon. Avoid having a huge dish of ice cream every night before bed. That's not smart snacking, and it will wreak havoc on your healthy eating plan. Be aware of what you eat during the day. By annotating your food journal for a week and evaluating it, you'll be able to see your trouble spots (like a big piece of chocolate every afternoon). Portion out snacks before eating. If you must snack on chips, pour a serving of chips onto a plate and eat only what's on the plate. If you eat from the bag, you'll eat a lot more than you planned.

The bottom line is that depriving yourself is never a good idea. You won't feel satisfied and you won't necessarily get any healthier. If you go a long time without eating, you're more likely to overeat at the next opportunity. So, if you're hungry, eat something. Stay conscious of what you're eating and keep yourself on a healthy eating plan. You must plan your meals, snacks and everything in between. Of course, remember to balance with a fitness plan. Remember, snacking is okay, but snack smartly!

"I can't keep a food journal. I'm too busy."

If you're too busy to journal, you're definitely too busy to mentally keep track of everything you eat and drink during the day. Think about what you ate for dinner last night. Think about all the components of the meal. Did you remember all of it? Did you get the butter you put on the food to make it taste better, the extra dressing you added to the salad because it needed a little more flavor, or the sample scoop of dessert before you ate the real one? I bet you didn't.

Now, try to remember your meal from five days ago. Compare it to what you just ate at your last meal. I bet you can't! That's why writing it down is the only way to accurately track what you're eating. You probably already carry some kind of paper or electronic date book or planner, so why not use it to record your eating habits? When you start tracking your intake, you'll be surprised at what you're eating. You may even want to track your moods, times of the month and what was happening each day to see if there is any correlation to what and how you are eating.

Try journaling for a week. Write down what you eat and when you eat it. Write everything down to the condiments on your sandwich. Be completely honest. You're doing this to learn about yourself and your food habits, not to punish yourself. After you journal for a week, review your journal and see where you can make eating and exercise changes Make some adjustments to both, then monitor for a few weeks and see if they are helping you reach your desired goal. Keep going if your actions are helping you achieve your goals. If not, make some changes and journal again for a couple of weeks.

Keep doing this until you find a combination that works best for you. If you are struggling to find that combination, have a professional (like myself) review your journal and give you some feedback. Sometimes, slight adjustments are all you need to get you where you want to go. When you track your eating and exercise, you can reflect back to where you began. You will be amazed at any changes you've made, and you won't even miss the junk listed in the old pages.

Journaling can also be a great way to keep track of your successes. You may not lose weight immediately and you'll occasionally doubt your ability to stick to the plan; but if you have a food/exercise journal, you can look back and see how you've made positive changes. Those positive changes in your habits will lead to positive changes in your body. Seeing change is the biggest motivator of all.

Yes, you're busy. That's still no excuse for not taking care of you!

"Some people are skinny no matter what. I'll never be like that."

Yes, some people are naturally thin. They don't exercise and they don't eat right, yet they don't gain weight. Skinny doesn't necessarily mean healthy. They may be skinny fat people. Those are people who are skinny on the outside, but have a high fat body composition. Chances are you may need to work a little harder to stay thin, and that's okay. Societal pressure to be thin is what contributes to eating disorders and other mental health issues. Being too thin isn't any better than being overweight.

Regardless of what the scale says, a healthy lifestyle is always good for your body. Less body fat isn't the only measure of a healthy body. I have had naturally lean and healthy clients suffer health issues because their body fat and cholesterol levels were through the roof. Once we adjusted their eating habits and substituted healthier foods, they saw significant changes in their body composition and were much healthier overall. Health changes can be external or internal changes such as a healthier heart and other functions.

Yes, it's easier for some people to stay thin. It may be much harder for you, but not impossible. You just have to be more aware of what you're eating and how you burn off your calories. You need to plan for the perfect food intake-to-exercise ratio.

As you work to get healthier, you need to accept the body you have and love it. If you are negative and talk down to yourself, that self-defeating mindset can throw you off track and you will likely quit and give up. That, my friend, is unacceptable. Love your body and realize there are some changes to be made. Make a plan and execute. Decide on your goals, set a plan and start working toward those smaller jeans or whatever it is you decided to achieve. Find a healthy lifestyle that will benefit you for years to come.

There are no guarantees you'll be happier when you lose weight. The same is true of people who are naturally thin; they aren't necessarily happier or healthier. Blood pressure and cholesterol are but a few of many other factors to consider.

You may never be super thin. It's important to remember that most people are not. You can only be the best you can be. Comparing yourself to other people is a dangerous trap. There will always be someone thinner and better looking. Conversely, there will always be someone heavier than you. Work with what you have and be the best version of yourself every single minute of every day.

"I'm naturally thin. I can eat whatever I want."

Not true. While it may be true that you're naturally thin, you cannot eat whatever you want. A healthy weight is one measure of a healthy body, but it's not the only one. Even if your blood pressure, cholesterol, blood sugar and other measurements are good now, there's no guarantee you will be healthy forever.

A healthy lifestyle has many benefits other than looking good in jeans. A balanced diet will give you more energy. Healthy foods are good for your skin, digestive system, your hair and many other things. Regardless of your body type, I guarantee you'll see benefits from eating healthy.

Sticking to a balanced diet is good for your body and your spirit. Knowing you are eating healthy makes you a good role model for your children and other people you influence. It will help you feel better because you are doing something good for yourself. The scale will never tell you as much as you tell yourself. Fill your body with good food so you can look back and be proud of what you are doing.

Like I mentioned earlier, comparing yourself to others is never a good idea. It's great that you're thin; now you can work on being healthy. If you're already healthy, keep up your habits and always look for ways to improve them.

"I'm afraid."

Most people don't come to a trainer and admit they're afraid. Often, people get close to their goals only to realize it wasn't everything they hoped it would be. They begin to fear the changes they see.

Lifestyle changes are scary. It's hard to give up the familiar. *How will others react? What if I can't do it or maintain what I'm doing? What if it doesn't make a difference?*

There are many reasons to be afraid, but if you're strong enough to change your lifestyle and change your eating habits, you're strong enough to conquer your fears. You've come this far, so don't let fear hold you back.

Let's examine some common fears my clients have shared with me. With a little work and planning, you'll learn you don't really need to be afraid.

Fear of love

With some reflection, you may find you have been hiding behind a less-than-ideal body. This may give you an excuse for any romantic failures you are currently experiencing in your life right now. If you develop a healthy lifestyle and a healthy body, you won't need that excuse. Staying heavy and out of shape is just another way of letting your overweight body control your life.

You need to be in charge of your body, not the other way around. Take your current "hot self" and get out there and live! Don't get complacent with where you are in building your healthy lifestyle. You have to love the body you're in AND have goals to improve your health status. Working on your body and overall health will enable you to work on your relationship (or lack thereof).

Healthy relationships are not just about looks. It's not always that simple. You need to feel confident, have positive self-talk and be willing to try new things to have the changes you seek. If you look at yourself in the mirror and don't see yourself as sexy, able and self-confident, it's likely your partner will pick up on this. That could be detrimental to your relationship. The better you feel and the healthier you are, the more prepared you will be for a healthy relationship.

Fear of failure

This is natural. Yes, you might fail; but if you work hard and follow your plan, I know you will have success. You will be able to look at your diet and be happy that you met your goals. You will be able to praise yourself for the small changes you have made along the way. If you work strategically every day, you will likely realize your desired successes. Don't be afraid. You definitely will not succeed if you don't try. Every journey starts with taking the first step. President Roosevelt said, "It is hard to fail, but it is worse to have never tried to succeed." You can accomplish your goals and dreams. You just need to START!

Fear of success

It's easy to hide behind and blame your failures on your unhealthy body. You tell yourself that you can't run as fast, can't walk as far, don't have the right bicycle, etc. In reality, you probably don't look or feel your best because you have not been taking care of yourself. This lack of self-care has caught up to you. Now you are not able to do the things you want to do or were once able to.

Maybe somewhere along life's pathway you have tried to change your health situation, but at the time you could not find the success you were working toward. Maybe in the back of your mind you were self-deprecating and were afraid you could not maintain what you were doing, so you gave up. Maybe you realized that if you take care of your body and meet your goals, you won't be able to use those excuses anymore, and that scares you. Dale Carnegie said, "Instead of worrying about what people say of you, why not spend time trying to accomplish something they will admire."

Good advice. Let's get to work! It's time for you to feel great and not have to use those excuses anymore. Eat right and get physical, and you will thank yourself for what you've done for *you*. You will be able to face yourself and celebrate your successes. Success with your body is something you get to see and live with on a daily basis. Drop the excuses and the fear and get to work so you can remember what you've done to make you a better version of yourself.

Fear of other people

Other people won't directly benefit from positive changes in your body. Only you will benefit from more energy, a sleek new look and a feeling of success. Other people may not be supportive or they may question your decision to take care of yourself, not because they don't want you to be healthy, but because they are afraid they may also have to change. They might even be jealous that you had the courage to make life-altering changes. They may try to sabotage you by trying to keep your old habits front and center in your life.

For example, your friend is not working on being healthy, so when he/she comes to visit they bring your favorite food, snack or beverage. Maybe they try to schedule an event during your regularly planned workout time. They may be afraid that if you look and feel better you may not want to maintain your friendship with them anymore. Or maybe they're afraid you are exercising and doing activities they aren't, which makes them feel bad about themselves. If they can sabotage your efforts, they won't have to change.

My advice to you is to carry out your plan to be healthy. It's about YOU feeling healthy, lean and strong. It's about YOU taking better care of yourself. Don't let anything or anyone stand in the way of you getting better. Your successes can be a good example to the people around you, so maybe they will take better care of themselves. That's a great feeling! Trust me, everyone around you will benefit from you feeling better.

The important thing is to remember that your lifestyle change is for you! You have to live with yourself every day. If you're healthy, you are the one who will benefit. If you're not, you are the one who will deal with the consequences.

"I take a vitamin, so I don't need to eat healthy."

Taking a multivitamin is a great idea and a great way to fulfill shortcomings in your diet; however, vitamins are supplements. They are meant to supplement the quality food you're already putting into your body, not replace it. Vitamins are less satisfying than food, and they don't provide the same benefits to your body as healthy foods.

There are many vitamin and mineral supplements on the market. Taking one multivitamin is a great way to make sure you get plenty of vitamins and minerals for your body. One multivitamin will give you some of the extras you need. It's a great way to fight off disease and keep your body chemistry balanced. Taking a handful of vitamins while eating poorly is not a substitute for filling your body with good food. Relying on multivitamins is not as healthy as eating healthy food.

Think about it this way: if you are sick, you wouldn't overdose on your over-the-counter medicine. More is not better. When you're sick, the proper amount of medicine is available to support your body's immune system. Taking more than suggested can be counterproductive and can actually do more harm than good (or kill you). Taking too many vitamins and not eating healthy can also have a negative effect on you. It's about finding the right combination and providing your body with some additional support.

"I don't eat bad foods."

Read this next sentence out loud, then repeat it: *There are no bad foods.* Sure, there are quality foods you should eat every day such as fresh fruits and vegetables, whole grains, low-fat dairy and lean protein. There are also foods which are lesser quality. I call these "sometimes" foods. No food is always bad. I've already mentioned the importance of treats. Most treats are considered bad, but I don't believe this. Have a treat sometimes, but in moderation.

No food should ever be forbidden. When you think a food is forbidden, you are likely to think like a little kid: *If it's forbidden, I'm going to have some!* The trick is to eat less-healthy foods in moderation. These foods are often tasty, and cravings for "sometimes" foods can be really strong. So, give in to the cravings—sometimes. Work it in and eat quality foods the rest of the time. Forbidding yourself from ever having your favorite sweet or salty snack will just make you want it more.

Foods themselves are not bad. Excess food is bad for you. Eating too much junk food is bad for you, but not bad in itself. You can't just label some foods as bad and stop eating them. Even healthy foods can have their bad points. Most fruits are high in sugar, but that doesn't mean you should give up fruit. Instead of labeling food as good or bad, try dividing food into "everyday" and "sometimes" categories. You'll be able to enjoy more food if you're not forbidden from anything. A balanced diet will come from eating a variety of foods. Cutting out one category of foods just means it'll be harder to get a complete and balanced diet.

"I can't eat healthy. I have kids."

Kids love "sometimes" foods. They're delicious. Kids aren't mature enough to understand that they can't eat or have everything they want. As an adult, you know it's okay to treat yourself sometimes as long as you eat healthy most of the time. Teach this strategy to your children. They can eat treats sometimes as long as they fill their bodies with healthy foods most of the time. Teach them to eat their meal first and finish with dessert.

Small children aren't able to prepare their own foods. As a family leader, this is where you come in. Your children will likely eat healthy vegetables if you serve them. They may protest and refuse to eat a certain food because they don't like the taste or texture. That's okay. Find another one they do like. Ultimately, you are in charge of what your children eat. It's fine to slip the "sometimes" food in with some of their favorites as long as you make sure they eat the healthy foods more often. If you include healthy foods as part of the meal, your children will likely eat them. Don't make a big deal out of it.

A strategy for promoting healthy eating with your children is to ensure you have more healthy food than junk food in the house. If they only have healthy options to choose from when they need a snack, they will eat the healthy foods. You should be doing the same thing for yourself. Don't buy junk food for the house. If it's a choice between a chocolate chip cookie and an apple, which would be the most likely choice for a snack? Make cookies a limited offer!

When our children were growing up, we provided fresh

vegetables and fruit in storage bags in the refrigerator. When they wanted a snack, all they had to do was grab a baggie and go. We limited the sugary and fat-filled options, so they took the healthy ones. Now, as adults, my children snack on fresh veggies and fruit when we get together for family events. We rarely eat chips because they didn't have them as an option when growing up. If we do have chips, it's usually a whole grain chip with salsa or avocado, so they still get their veggies.

It is important to give your children treats the way you give yourself treats. Giving a child macaroni and cheese occasionally is fine. If your children love hot dogs, give them a hot dog once in a while. Serve the hot dog with a side of their favorite fruit and a glass of milk to power up the overall value of the meal. Also, feed your children chicken, fish and other lean proteins along with other foods that create a balanced diet.

I have three children. Some nights, we would eat broccoli stir-fry with chicken. Sometimes, we had raw vegetables as a side dish. Other times, I took my kids to the pizza buffet and let them have whatever they wanted. We worked it in. When children grow up with a variety of healthy foods in their diet, they are more likely to love them as they get older.

It's hard to change your eating habits as an adult. It can be a difficult transition to go from a steady diet of carbs and fat to a balanced diet. Think of the gift you can give your children by teaching them good eating habits right from the beginning. That way, they won't need to learn later in life how to remove junk from their diet.

Parents should be very careful to ensure their children eat

healthy when they are young. *No dessert until after you've finished dinner!* You should be serving a fruit or vegetable and a glass of milk at each meal to set an example that not all treats need frosting or sugar in them. As a parent, you should make sure your children are not snacking all day while watching TV. Are you leading with the right examples? If you take care of yourself, you will automatically take better care of your children. They will grow up learning that eating healthy is a good way to maintain a healthy lifestyle. You will give them habits they can carry forward for the rest of their lives.

"I can't make healthy meals for just one person."

Cooking for one person is just like cooking for a crowd. If you can make a tasty, healthy meal for a group of people, you can make it for yourself. Just freeze any leftovers in meal-size portions for later meals. This allows you to take out a prepared healthy meal and heat it for fast eating.

A common trap single people fall into is not making meals for themselves. They end up grazing all day and eating in front of the TV, at fast food restaurants or from convenience store counters. You are way better off preparing a meal (even a simple one) than taking one of the options above.

Make a meal, put it on a plate, sit at the table and eat it. Take this time to do something good for you and your body. This helps you in multiple ways. Putting food on a plate will help you see the portions you are actually eating. Sitting down at the table will help you realize you are eating, which can help you eat more slowly. Your food will be more satisfying if you take the time to enjoy it. You'll actually taste it and you won't be as hungry later.

If you dread taking the time to eat and clean up, pretend you're having guests or act like your parents are coming over. You wouldn't serve them off a plate balanced on the couch, so give yourself the same courtesy. Eating healthy is good for your body and your spirit. Treat yourself as well as you treat your guests.

Living alone also gives you the advantage of being in total control of what goes on in the kitchen. You buy the food, so make sure you always have a good supply of your healthy favorites. You make the meals, so you choose which nights are healthy and which nights you are going to splurge. Your whole diet revolves around you, so take advantage of that.

Being healthy when you're single means it will be easier to be healthy if and when you have a family. You'll already have good habits to share with those you love. If you remain single, you'll be happy and confident knowing you're doing all you can for your body. Doing something good for yourself is always a good choice, no matter what!

"My family demands unhealthy foods."

This is another way of blaming someone else for your bad habits. If you're living with someone (or several) who don't want to eat the same foods as you do, don't push yourself on them. Just buy and prepare smaller portions of healthy foods for yourself. It may even work to substitute small amounts of healthy foods for what the others are already eating.

It's ridiculous to believe that anyone not interested in

having better health will start eating well right away. For example, they may not know if you're scrambling some eggs with a few of the yokes removed. They may not notice if you start replacing some of the butter in your baking recipe with applesauce. Try using leaner meat in place of fatty red meat. Many seasoning blends have lower-salt versions that taste the same as saltier ones. Buy frozen yogurt or cool whip instead of ice cream. Instead of serving a sour cream-based dip with crackers, try some high-protein hummus with crackers (or raw veggies). It may take a little creativity, but you can do it.

You may never convince your family that eating healthy food is a better choice for them, but you may surprise them with some simple substitutions. If they compliment you on a new recipe, tell them about the substitutions and how they have less calories and fat. It's a win for you and your loved ones.

This is really where role modeling comes in. If the people you live with see you making healthy food choices and losing weight, they may be intrigued and will be more likely to try healthy eating. You can only control what you're eating. It all starts with you.

"I'm gone a lot and have to eat out."

We all know it can be hard to eat healthy when you eat out. There are plenty of tasty choices that are covered in sauce, cheese, or fried. But those aren't the only delicious things at a restaurant. You could choose a baked item, not a fried one. Or you could order grilled foods that have a nice smoked flavor. Most restaurants will allow you to choose vegetables on the side instead of fries. Don't be afraid to get a doggie bag and pack up half your meal before you start eating. That way, you'll have a tasty meal for tomorrow and you won't be as likely to overeat. Offer to split a meal with someone. Splitting a meal gives you a great bonding opportunity (and you'll be saving money).

In most restaurants, the meal portions are way more than any single person should eat, so there's no need for an appetizer and dessert with the meal. If you'd like to sample a starter or a dessert, split it with others at the table. Better yet, just order a side salad (easy on the dressing). That extra bulk of food will help you feel fuller when you finish eating. Tell yourself you'll be satisfied with only a few extra bites. You'll be able to button your pants after the meal and will feel better.

Sharing food is an important experience among family and friends. You don't have to give that up just because you're making a healthy lifestyle change. Making changes for yourself can benefit others around you. We've all been with friends or family who stand up at the end of a meal and proclaim how stuffed they are. I guarantee that if you share a meal with the right attitude, you will walk away feeling full and will have consumed half the calories you would have eaten otherwise.

My husband and I do this. He is a big guy who grew up in the "clean plate" era. He would eat a big meal and likely take items left over from my plate. I convinced him he did not need to eat that much food. One day, I talked him into sharing a meal with me while we were out to eat. He was worried he wasn't going to get enough. When we finished eating, he proclaimed he was full. The bill was half the price and we left the plate clean!

If you are at a restaurant with a salad bar or buffet, be careful. Commit to only having one plate of food and don't cheat by overloading the plate. Just because you are at the salad bar doesn't mean everything there is healthy. Think about those dressings and the tossed mayo-based salads. Fat is fat, whether it comes from vegetable oil or fat-based salads.

Typically, you aren't paying much more for an all-you-can-eat buffet over a regular menu item. Make the all-you-*should*-eat line healthier by taking one plate of well-balanced foods. If you cannot find healthy food options at the buffet, I would suggest you not return. Think of the bloated feeling you will have if you eat too much, then choose to eat less.

It's also important to keep track of what you're drinking at a restaurant. There are many calories in most drinks, including soda. Drinking three or four beverages with your meal can add more sugar and calories without adding nutrition. Enjoy one beverage, then drink water. You'll be more satisfied and happier with your meal while making good choices for your body.

If you've decided to go out for the evening and have a few drinks, remember to work them into your daily intake. Beware of the sugary and fatty foods that often come with a night of drinking. Eat a balanced meal before you go out so you won't be tempted to grab munchies after a few drinks. Remember, late night snack foods still count for that day in your food journal. It's okay to slide on very rare occasions, but don't overdo it with frequent celebrations.

"I'm going to die anyway.
I might as well eat what I want."

Yes, you will eventually die, regardless of your lifestyle and habits. Wouldn't it be more fun to look hot while you're alive, though? You can have the confidence that only comes with healthy living and a great body if you watch what you are putting in your mouth. You can live longer and healthier by exercising and eating healthier. You can have energy to live a full, active life and do the things you want to do. You can feel good in smaller clothes. Finally, when you eventually die, you don't have to be buried in an extra-large casket.

If you focus your energy on thoughts of dying, you will likely become depressed and start feeling like you don't have anything to live for. Depression makes you feel hopeless. Eventually, you won't be able to enjoy each day you're alive. It all comes back to the old song, *Accentuate the Positive*. Focus on the positive things in your life. Focus on doing everything you can to live your best life. Be in good shape so you can live. I see so many people who just sit through life. They are too heavy and they don't care for themselves. They live like they are already dead. Don't be one of those people!

You may be saving money for retirement. Think of a healthy lifestyle in the same way. If you make a few sacrifices now, you can live a better life when you're older. Yes, it would be great to have that money in the short term. By eating healthy and establishing an exercise routine now, you've chosen to make your golden years a little more golden. You want to be able to do the things you enjoy when you're older and have fun!

You're not dead yet. Live your life as long as you can and enjoy it. Don't be a victim of your past life. Maybe you can't conquer your family's genes or years of bad habits, but you can do your part *now* to live a healthier life. Take charge and live as well and as happily as you can. I believe that living happily means eating healthy so you can have the energy to do what you want when you want. You can live longer so you can spend more time with your friends and loved ones. You'll have more opportunities to do things throughout your later years. You won't have to worry constantly about your body. Eat healthy, exercise, keep your mind strong, take charge of yourself and live while you're alive.

"I love my body the way it is."

Do you really; or is that what you say to yourself to avoid having to face your reality? It's awesome if you have a healthy body image. It's great to love yourself and love the body you have. However, I know you will feel better about your beautiful body when you know you're doing everything in your power to keep it healthy and strong. Making improvements in any part of your life allows you to feel more satisfied. Having a healthy body will make you even more appreciative of it and what you can do with it. You'll love every muscle you've built, every curve you've formed and every movement you make. You'll feel even better about that great body you've got if you start taking care of it now.

Love your body. Love it full of healthy foods and love all the hard work you've put into it. You work hard for other things you want (new car, new outfits, shoes), so why not work hard to get or keep the body you want? Every time you walk by a mirror, you'll love what you see and you'll love the body you created by working out and eating properly.

If you don't have the body you want yet, get to work on it. It all starts with you. It is important to remember to love yourself throughout the entire process. When you see progress in the form of looser-fitting pants or having more energy and stamina at the end of the day, celebrate! You're on your way to a better body. It may take some time to get to your ideal body, so be sure to celebrate the body you have throughout the entire process. Speak positive words to yourself and you will breed more positivity.

"I feel fine."

You probably do feel fine—mostly. Maybe you've learned to live with a few aches and pains. Maybe you don't sleep well and feel tired during the day. Maybe you have to struggle to put on your favorite clothes or they pinch you in certain places when you do get them on.

The truth is that you don't know how good you can feel until you feel good. You don't know how bad you were feeling until you feel better. Losing weight and eating healthy isn't a cure for everything, but it can help reduce joint pain and make it easier to move around. It gives you more energy and lets you do more of the things you want to do. It also puts less strain on your heart and circulatory system, which helps you live longer.

Being healthy will give you even more time to enjoy your body and the things you like to do because you will feel stronger. Eating better and exercising will allow you to have a healthier body and will help you feel better.

It's no secret that weighing less will take pressure off your joints. It's less work to move a lighter body, so you'll be able to do more activities. Imagine how good you can feel and enjoy the benefits that come with a healthier body. Living healthier also lowers your risk for diseases such as diabetes, heart disease or high blood pressure. Overall, living healthier will keep you living longer and give you the ability to do the things you love with the people you love!

"I have great genes. I'll likely live to a ripe old age, anyway."

Fantastic! Good genes do give you a better shot at living longer, but they aren't the end-all be-all. Having good genes will likely have a positive impact on your overall lifespan. However, when you combine it with eating healthy and exercising, you will have a winning combination as you age. You will likely diminish the genetic effect if you eat fatty foods, drink alcohol, smoke, don't exercise and ignore your mental well-being. We probably all know someone who lived to be 100 who had bacon and whole milk at every meal. They were either really lucky or they took additional steps to keep themselves healthy.

Think about it this way: If you plan to live until whatever is old to you, you should be prepared for it. You probably have (or should have) a savings account earmarked for retire- . ment. You're saving now so that when you get older you'll have resources to make choices about what your retirement will look like. Maybe you'll choose to travel. Maybe your goal is to stay in your own home and do the things you couldn't do when you were working full time. Ultimately, whatever you are going to do takes planning.

Keeping your body in shape is like your savings account. Stay healthy now and it will give you the ability to make lifestyle choices as you age. Travel won't be nearly as fun if you can't get out of your chair, are too weak to walk or weigh too much to fit in an airplane seat. Maybe your internal organs won't function well because you didn't take care of yourself earlier in life.

If you don't have the energy to move when you are older, you may not be able to live alone for long. Staying healthy gives you the ability to spend more time doing the things you like to do. Give yourself the gift of a healthy body now so you can live and be active for as long as you can.

If you eat good foods, eat in moderation and exercise while you're young (or at your current age), you'll be better able to live the life you want as you age. You don't want to be forced to radically change your lifestyle because of a medical emergency later on in life.

Many people will only start to eat well, exercise or take care of themselves after they get older or after a medical issue such as a heart attack, high blood pressure, high cholesterol, adult-onset diabetes, etc. These life events cause people to immediately and radically change how they live. They are required to go on special diets, modify the foods they are eating or start exercising. They will now work harder at regulating their bodies or overcoming a medical issue that could have been avoided had they invested in their well-being earlier.

"I just can't get motivated to eat healthy."

It's hard to get motivated to eat well when you've spent your whole life eating whatever you want. It's difficult to make drastic, sudden changes. It's even harder when everyone around you is eating what they want. The temptation to eat with others and eat what they're eating is always around you.

Americans have spent their whole lives surrounded by food at family events, in stores, at sporting venues, etc.—and that's the problem. It's hard to say no to something you have easy access to. It takes self-control, discipline and a strong will to stay true to your healthy eating plan.

If you want to see what food means to some people, spend time around those who can't eat what they want. Visit a nursing home or a hospital where the patients can't eat. Spend time with people who can only have a few sips of water or a few bites of mush.

I think about my own food choices when I picture my grandfather in the hospital with cancer. He begged to have someone swab his mouth with water because he was so parched. He had to eat all his meals through a tube. When you see someone who desperately wants food and isn't able to have any, it makes you realize how trivial your problems with food really are. My grandfather could not control what he ate or how he ate it. YOU can!

Part of the problem with eating healthy is that it's so easy to get caught up in the short-term. If all you can think about is how good an extra slice of pizza would taste right now, it's hard to imagine if giving up that slice would have long-term results on your body. If you're hungry and you want to grab something from the drive-thru, it's hard to imagine how taking a few extra minutes to make a healthier choice will be better for you in the long run.

Planning ahead is key. If you know you're going to be tempted with foods that don't have a lot of nutritional value, decide before you leave the house or office how much and what you will eat. Then, when you get to your destination, eat what you've planned for and nothing more. Keep a high-protein granola bar or trail mix in your desk or car for a quick healthy snack.

Don't put yourself in a position to overindulge just because you're caught in the moment. Eat right earlier in the day so won't be starving. You'll then be able to fend off the temptation of something that's not healthy for you.

Healthy food can be delicious. Look at them as a way to nourish your body instead of considering nutritious food as some sort of punishment. Spend time planning for and getting good nutrition. This should extend the time you get to live healthy. Good food is right for you. You'll be happier and healthier by treating it as a life necessity.

Think about how good you could feel if you ate right and were exercising. Think about what you do and what you eat as you go through your day. Think about your healthy lifestyle goals for the day. That should motivate you to eat and exercise in a manner that will allow you to feel better now and into your future.

We all know it's hard to get motivated. Getting something you want may mean giving up something else you probably want. Use self-talk to push you back to your positive way of thinking. Have some go-to phrases you can repeat to yourself when you are tempted to eat something you know is not in your plan. Think about what will allow you to feel better as you eat. Is one more slice of pizza with your friends the best thing for you? Can you motivate yourself to say, "No, thank you," so you can maintain a healthy, lean body. Use your motivation to say no today so you can live a healthier tomorrow.

My husband loves chocolate. Every time he goes to the local hardware store and is getting ready to check out, he is faced with the challenge of buying a candy bar that is so conveniently placed at eye level. *Should I pass, knowing it's not what is best for me?* He repeats the phrase, "I am living healthy, happy, lean and strong," until he gets past the check-out stand and is in the parking lot. This has helped him avoid the enemy's voice: *Go ahead. One king size candy bar isn't going to kill you.* What is your phrase? If you don't have one, get one!

"I can't stand wasting food."

A lot of us grew up being told we needed to eat everything on our plates so we could get a prize (dessert). Maybe you remember being told, "Eat everything on your plate because there are starving people somewhere in the world." We became members of the Clean Plate Club.

This may have sounded reasonable when we were younger, but we should know better as adults. True, food does cost money and it's frustrating to throw it down the garbage disposal. It can be especially frustrating if you spent time preparing a lovely meal only to have people not eat it.

No one was trying to hurt you when they were teaching you to eat all your food. They just didn't know any better.

We do now. The problem is that eating everything in front of you often results in eating too much. If there is too much food on your plate, you shouldn't feel like you have to eat it all. Eat until you are satisfied, not until you meet an arbitrary goal such as a clean plate. Take the leftovers and put them away or freeze them for a later meal or snack. Don't let guilt override your healthy eating plan. You have planned for what you can eat. Eat that, then quit.

After eating right-sized portions for a while, you'll notice how much food it takes to make you feel full. You'll start filling your plate with just enough food to satisfy you, and your plate will be clean. It's a win-win.

If you are given a large plate of food, it is up to you to make smart decisions about what you will eat. An ideal plate portion is about half vegetables and should contain a big chunk of lean protein plus a small starch and a small amount of fat. Most plates actually contain a big starch with some protein, a fairly good amount of fat, and perhaps a small serving of vegetables.

When presented with a plate full of food, divide it into healthy portions of each item and eat those. Leave the rest for another time. Remember, you are doing what is best for you. Don't clean your plate or eat more than you should just to make someone else feel good. If they question you, just tell them you are working on being happy, healthy, lean and strong and that you are watching your food intake. Then compliment them on an awesome meal.

Dessert is another area where the clean plate concept

can get you in trouble. Instead of cake and ice cream, pick your favorite of the two and pass on the other one. Don't be afraid to ask for a smaller piece than what the host has served you. You could also divide the dessert in half as you eat and explain to your host that you are to full from the awesome meal to eat the whole thing.

If you are in a restaurant, ask your server if you can substitute fresh fruit for your dessert. Many restaurants offer pancakes along with eggs. They will allow you to substitute fruit for hashbrowns or pancakes. I do this all the time.

When you eat dessert, have it on a small plate because it will make the dessert look bigger. As mentioned earlier, it is important to always eat off a plate. Don't just eat out of the bag or directly from the pan. Portion control is much easier when it is limited from the start. Yes, washing dishes is a chore; but washing an extra dish in exchange for a trimmer waist and a healthy body is a fair trade.

Snacking is another area where it's easy to eat more than you should. You sit down with a bag of chips, a large bag of candy or something similar, then you start chatting with someone or watching TV. Before you know it, you have eaten everything! Now, you are mad at yourself for eating more than you wanted. Negative self-talk begins and the enemy speaks up: *See, you don't have any self-control!* Then, you spiral into your old habits. Don't do that to yourself.

The easiest way to avoid this dilemma is to serve yourself a snack on a small plate or in a small bowl. Eat the snack you served yourself, then stop eating. Don't just grab a bag, carton or pan of something and start eating. Snacking is fine, but enjoy your snack. Don't just put something in your mouth and chew. Take the time to enjoy the taste while you eat it. When the snack is gone, stop eating. Remember, you are not responsible for cleaning out the container. Most food labels show you what the serving size is and give you the nutritional breakdown. Pay attention to that information and use it to your benefit.

In addition, never eat something you don't want or need from someone else's plate to make their plate clean. They may not want the extra calories, either. A quick taste during dinner is fine, but don't absentmindedly munch your kids' leftovers while you're cleaning up. You've already eaten your meal, so there's no need to eat more.

"There's so much nutritional advice out there. Who do I listen to?"

There's always a new diet or plan guaranteed to help you lose weight and feel better. There's always someone out there who has invented a revolutionary supplement to reduce fat and build muscle. There's a lot of money to be made in helping people feel better about themselves, and there are many people who want to get their hands on some of it. If people would just spend a little more money on quality foods, they wouldn't need crazy supplements or quick-fix body plans.

Think about where you want to invest your money and your time. If you want to contribute to someone's get-rich-quick plan, join their fad diet. Otherwise, spend your time and money on quality foods, and exercise for at least 10 minutes a day.

Most fad diet plans focus on cutting something out such as fats, carbs, sugar, red meat, or eating after 7:00 pm. They all require cutting it out of your diet completely. If you have the discipline to completely remove some of your favorite foods from your diet, you have more willpower than most people. Even if they aren't your favorite foods, you'll eventually miss them and revert back to eating them.

Many people lose a lot of weight in a short time by cutting things out of their diet. Most of them put it all back (and sometimes more) when they go off the plan and resume eating normally. People go off their plan because it's too hard to maintain. They want to eat their favorite foods again. When they allow themselves to break their diet, they go nuts and eat whatever they want. This is not the right way to maintain a healthy body and mind.

If you look closely, most long-lasting nutrition plans have a few things in common: drink plenty of water; eat fresh foods, including fruits and veggies; and watch your sugar and salt intake. These basic foundations of healthy eating will help everyone lose weight and feel better.

You don't have to completely cut anything out. Just be mindful of what you're eating. Maybe you won't lose 10 pounds this week, but you will eventually lose 10 pounds and keep it off. You'll be happy because you're doing something good for your body and won't feel deprived. You'll also be very happy with the results. It is often said that it takes 21 days of doing the same thing to build a new habit. Stay consistent. Eventually, you will achieve the results you want.

I work with a number of clients who have had bariatric procedures. At the beginning, they lose a lot of weight because their stomachs have been surgically altered. If they improve their eating and exercising habits in combination with the procedure, they are likely to reap the benefits of the surgery for life. The key here is that they must change their lifestyle. If they revert to eating poorly and without exercise, they will likely gain back all their weight; and the medical procedure will have been in vain.

"So, all this is well and good; but what do I do to start?"

Let's bring some closure to this nutrition section. The thing about a healthy eating plan is that it's different for everyone. Some people do need more calories than others, but don't just decide to be one of those people. Unless you're extremely active, you don't need additional calories. Some people have specific needs that require them to limit or increase their consumption of various foods. Some people may have allergies to certain foods.

Figure out what works for you. You can either do this through trial and error or get professional advice. Either way, convince yourself that it's time to get started. Tell yourself this will be hard work and that there will be ups and downs along the way. Start today, not tomorrow or Monday. I suggest you try the following, which has worked well for so many of my clients:

Start journaling.
Write down everything you eat as soon as you eat it. If you don't write it down as soon as you eat it, you likely won't remember everything you consumed throughout the day. You'll be eating all kinds of food during the day and you will consume all kinds of calories, sugars and fats that will sneak

through and not be counted. Try it for a few weeks to gauge your average eating habits. Journaling can help you think about what you're eating before you put it into your mouth. If you are going to feel bad about logging a donut with your coffee, then don't eat the donut.

After journaling for a few weeks, review it and see where you can make changes. If you have access to a dietitian, trainer or someone who follows a healthy eating plan, have them take a look and suggest changes. You may notice that you eat a high-fat, low-nutrient snack every day after work. You can choose to replace it with a quality high-protein food. You may learn that you drink more than one can of soda per day. You can modify your plan so you drink more water instead. Journaling helps you be aware of what you are putting into your body. What you are putting into your body affects your well-being.

Only make one change at a time.
Many times, people make a list of everything they want to change in order to get healthy. It overwhelms them and they quit before they start. It took you many years and several bad habits to get where you are right now. Don't expect to change everything overnight. Give your body and yourself time to get used to the changes you are making. After a while, you'll find you don't even miss your old ways of eating and exercising.

Start with a simple change so you can feel success instantly. When you've made a few simple changes, try something harder. Focus your meals on lean proteins and vegetables. Replace white carbs with whole grains. Journaling can give you a history of what worked and what didn't. Journal your exercise routines, how you felt during a particular day or week, what was happening in your life, etc. See how these events affect your diet (the foods you eat, not an eating plan). Find out what worked and avoid those that did not help you reach your goal of living happier, healthier and stronger.

Watch your portion sizes and what you are eating.
Eating fewer calories will help you lose weight. A smaller amount of food will mean fewer calories going in and less for you to burn off. I would suggest you eat smaller, more frequent meals and snacks. I probably eat 7-8 times a day, but in small healthy portions so I don't feel like I'm lacking something in my diet. If you do the same, you probably won't overeat at mealtime, miss the extra food, and definitely won't miss the extra weight.

Make good choices.
You can eat the foods you love, but eating one thing you love means eating less of something you don't like as much. Have a treat, but don't have treats on a regular basis. Decide in advance what you're going to eat each day. Then decide how you can make that work into your daily eating plan. Exchange a carb-filled breakfast for a high-protein break-fast and enjoy a few extra carbs later in the day. Skip dessert and have a glass of wine. You can have anything you want in moderation; you just can't have everything you want.

After you've done the hard work and changed your habits, it's time to do the easy thing: watch your body change. Don't stop your good habits when you see results. You are seeing these changes because you are changing the way you eat and exercise. The longer you stick with it, the easier it will be and the better you will feel and look. You have to stick with your program. It will work.

It's important to understand that you may not lose weight every week and will eventually plateau. *Well, I guess the hard work I put in this week didn't pay off. I might as well give up!* Don't think that way. Instead, make some minor adjustments to your plan and push yourself to continue moving forward. Nothing worthwhile is easy, especially losing weight and getting a healthier body.

Remember, it is important to plan, execute, review, make changes and celebrate your results. Get to work on your new nutrition plan. Believe in yourself and always celebrate your results. You can do this!

Activity vs. Idleness

You've probably heard the following: *You have to have a balanced diet and an exercise plan. Diet and exercise are the two most important components of a healthy life. Diet with exercise is the way to lose weight and keep it off.* You learned that you must master a healthy diet in the previous section. Now let's take some time to talk about the importance of exercise in your life.

Exercise is a necessary component of any healthy lifestyle. Change your diet and you'll lose some weight. Cutting calories is great. Combine a healthy diet with an additional calorie-burning exercise program and you'll lose dramatically more weight and be unstoppable.

Exercise, in its simplest form, is moving. It doesn't have to be a triathlon. For you, it may mean getting off the couch and going for a walk. It's a cumulative process; the more you exercise, the more your body will need exercise. As you master one level of fitness, you can increase the amount or intensity of exercise. Give it a few months and you'll be amazed at what you can do.

When you start out, you may be unable to walk around the block. Work at it, and eventually you may be able to run a 10-minute mile. You'll build stamina and be able to do more during the day. Walking up the stairs will get easier. You'll be better able to keep up with your children. You'll lift more, get more flexible and become less prone to injury. You will look better and feel better. You may even sleep better; and if your sex life is waning, it may improve that as well.

People think about exercise like they do with healthy eating. Everyone knows they should do it and everyone has excuses for why they don't. The truth is that everyone needs exercise. Your body is built for activity, so move it around. See what resonates for you in the following pages. Some of these excuses may sound familiar. Let's find a way to get you moving!

"I don't have time to exercise."

Yes, you do! You don't want to bank your minutes and save them for when you are recovering from a medical wakeup call. Maybe you don't have time for an hour of cardio and an hour of strength training and a half hour of toning every day. You have a life and your life is busy and full of things you "have" to do. You just need to make exercise one of those things. You may even find that exercise gives you more time.

You'll have more energy to get your tasks done. You'll have better stamina and be better able to keep moving all day long. You'll live longer, so you'll have more months and years to do what you want.

The thing about getting in better shape is that you can

do it with the time you have. If you have three hours a day to devote to working out, you will see dramatic results in your body in a short time. If you don't have that much time, you can do a little at a time and still see results.

The secret is to schedule your workout into your busy schedule. Take a look at your day and determine when you can fit in some activity. It doesn't have to be a big, sweaty event. Start by finding a 10-minute chunk of time. Take that 10 minutes and do some physical activity. Then, stretch that out to 15 or 20 minutes. Eventually, you'll discover you are working out for half an hour. Use half your lunch break to go for a walk. Take the kids out for a bike ride. Walk to the store to pick up a loaf of bread. Do the things you already have to do. Just put a little thought into how you can turn them into a workout.

Making time for your body is as important as making time for anything else. Busy people deserve the benefits of exercise. We all want people in authority (the president, your boss, our parents) to be healthy and in good shape. You want them to live happy, healthy, lean and strong lives so you have more time to be with them because they are important to you. To someone else, you might be their most important person. They want you to exercise and take care of yourself.

It's important enough to make it a regular part of your day. My mother is 81 years young. She starts every morning with her exercise routine and a 2-mile walk uptown with her girlfriends. For that, I am thankful. Because she takes care of herself, we are able to spend more time doing things together.

"I don't like to exercise."

You probably haven't found the exercise you like. You may not like to run, lift weights or swim; but chances are you like to do something—walk, yoga, dance, ride a bike, skate, golf, ski, etc. If it will help, take a friend with you, use headphones, or do whatever you have to do to get yourself moving. Even shoveling, raking and walking the dog are great for your body. Toning, stretching or any type of activity can be considered exercise. You just have to get up and get moving.

Activity doesn't have to involve counting or taking your pulse, or even sweating. Simply doing something means your body is getting the benefits of movement. If you do something you like, you are more likely to keep doing it and won't see it as exercise.

Changing your activity level is just like changing your eating habits. You must plan how to start doing it. Find a way to make your daily activities fit into your exercise plan. Strap on some in-line skates or go to the beach and walk up and down the shoreline. Meet your friends and play a game of one-on-one. Have a pillow fight with the kids. Just get out there and get started.

Exercise and activity shouldn't be things you hate. No one likes doing things they "have" to do. Don't think of it as exercise or a chore. Think of it as going for a hike, taking the kids to the park or mowing the lawn. This will ignite your internal furnace, which needs fuel to burn. Your body looks for fuel within itself and starts to burn the calories you have provided it. The more the furnace works, the more calories it burns.

Your body is like a bonfire. When you start the fire, you make a pile of wood and ignite it. As you add more wood, the fire gets hotter. It burns the wood faster, and you need more wood to keep it going. If you don't add more wood to the fire, it slowly dies out. The logs that did not burn just lay within the scorched earth. Calories are like that. If you get your body burning hotter, it will consume more calories. If you don't exercise and keep your internal fire burning, the calories find a spot on your body to lay, eventually causing you to become overweight and out of shape.

You can learn to love exercise. Think about how much you'll love wearing a smaller size and having more energy at the end of every day. Your body was designed to work and move. Your body loves stretching and being flexible. Exercise gets the blood flowing and gets your muscles ready for your daily activities.

You have to make exercise a regular part of your day. Eventually, you will get to a point where you literally have to do some type of activity every day just to feel balanced. Time to move and get your fire burning!

"I get bored exercising."

It's easy to get bored in a gym while running on the tread-mill and watching the guy in front of you endlessly climbing stairs. It's easy to get bored doing the same video routine every day at 7:00 am. So, don't do that. Find a few things you like to do and mix them up on a regular basis.

Do something different every day. If you can only find one exercise you like, find a way to spice it up. Try a new location or a new workout buddy or a new level of intensity. Find a way to not make it boring. Anything you like doing that involves moving your body counts as working out. If you love doing something, you won't get bored doing it.

There are a million types of exercise. You can certainly take 10 minutes out of your day to do one of them. You don't have to do the same thing every day. Pick a physical activity you enjoy and would do even if it weren't considered exercise. Take a dance class. Explore new neighborhoods on a run or walk. Join a group of people training for a race and make new friends. You can have fun with exercise.

Make it a game, even if the idea of competing gives you flashbacks of being the last one picked for dodgeball back in your school days. Remember, the only person you need to compete with is yourself.

A game can be simple: Run until the end of the song in your playlist. Keep up in aerobics a little better than yesterday. Walk on the treadmill through your favorite show. Bowl 10 strikes in a row. Ride your bike .01 miles farther today than you did yesterday.

If making it a game doesn't work, think about all the good you're doing for yourself as you exercise. I know you won't get tired of people complimenting you: *You're looking great. Your body is building muscle and you look stronger. Wow, what are you doing to look so healthy?* Tell yourself you won't get tired of having a leaner, firmer and sexier body. My husband and I used to tell our kids, "Only boring people get bored." Don't be boring!

"I'm on my feet all day. My job is physical."

There's no reason to skip your workout, even if you're tired at the end of the day. Lying down on the couch and vegging in front of the TV won't give you any extra energy. Plopping down in your favorite chair won't give you any more stamina. If you're constantly working only the muscles you use during the course of your workday, you'll continue to be tired and achy and out of balance at the end of every day.

The thing about work activity is that each day tends to be the same. You need to periodically get more challenging levels of activity. If you're doing the same routine every day, you aren't challenging your other muscles to make them stronger.

No matter what your daily level of activity is at your job, you're not getting a total body workout from it. If you're in a job with a lot of walking, you're likely to end up with strong calf muscles and sore feet. Conversely, the muscles in front of your legs will be weaker and your legs will ache because they are not in balance. You'll then need to find an exercise to strengthen the front leg muscles. You may have lower back pain. If so, work your core to make your back stronger and feel better. If you're lifting heavy things all day, add stretching to keep your muscles limber.

Repetitive motion injuries are caused by only working one part of your body over and over. It causes weakness in parts of the body and can be the root of injury. Muscles tend to come in pairs (e.g., biceps partner with triceps, quadriceps partner with hamstrings). If you only work half the pair, you'll see half the benefits of working the entire group. You'll become more developed in one area, which isn't good for your body.

Your activity plan should incorporate unused muscles as part of your daily activities. Design activities to work the opposing muscles so you can stay balanced. There is likely some part of the body you're not working. Find it and work on it. Don't let your health be defined by your job activity level and don't let your job take over your body.

"If I exercise, I'll just eat more."

See if this sound familiar: "Working out burns calories. That means I can eat more calories during the day. In fact, it means I can eat as much of my favorite foods as I want. Exercise is good for me. So, for the rest of the day, I don't have to worry about things that are good for me. I can eat and do whatever I want because I worked out today."

Sadly, that's not the way it works. That thinking doesn't hold up because there are no foods that are always bad for you. To burn fat, you need to work off more calories than you take in, period. You must do weight-bearing exercises on a regular basis to build muscle and tone your body. To show off those beautiful muscles, you have to reduce the layer of fat covering them. Exercising without eating right is only half the equation.

When you first start exercising, you may find you are more hungry than usual. You have burned more calories than usual and your body needs extra fuel (bonfire analogy). Don't undo all the good you've done by stuffing yourself full of junk. Add a small serving of quality foods high in protein.

If you exercise after work and you're usually starving by the time you finally get home, have a small snack in the afternoon. If you can't stand to eat before your morning workout, try a piece of fruit or a glass of milk. You'll feel full, you'll have energy for your workout, and you won't undo all the benefits of your exercise.

If you're hungry, eat something and journal it. Be aware of when you're hungry and when you're not. If you need to be doing something with your mouth, try chewing gum or drinking water. If you're bored, do something to engage your mind (maybe this is your chance to sneak in a workout). If you just want something sweet, find a healthier way to do it.

If you really are hungry, have a snack. A healthy lifestyle doesn't mean punishing yourself with an empty stomach. Have a small snack to ward off hunger, and record it in your food journal. Then, go about your day and get in your workout.

Before your workouts, eat quality carbs such as wholegrain cereals, high protein yogurts, whole grain pasta or fresh fruits and vegetables. This will give your body immediate fuel to burn when you begin your routine. Make sure you drink a lot of water before, during and after your workouts.

After your workouts, eat proteins such as fish, chicken, quinoa, avocado, dark leafy greens, or make yourself a protein shake. This will help you rebuild muscles and give you more energy for the rest of your day.

My rule of thumb is to only work out on days you plan to eat. If you're not planning to eat all day (not healthy) or if you're in bed with the flu, it's probably not as important; but get some physical activity any other time.

"I have a desk job and I work 24/7."

I've had clients who were truckers, executives, factory workers, stay-at-home parents and desk jockeys. I've worked with all of them to find ways to exercise. You can do it. The world won't end if you stop working for 10 minutes. If you're chained to your desk, pull in your abs for a count of 10, do butt clenches or sneak in some neck rolls. Bend your ankles, flex your fingers and do a few knee bends. Walk across the office to talk to someone instead of calling them. Not only will this get you in better shape, it will also make you a better worker. You won't be as tense, and taking a few minutes for a break will give your brain a rest and make you better able to focus.

Exercise is a great stress reliever. Take some time to unwind and work out the stiffness. Even if you don't think your body is suffering from being hunched over the keyboard, think about the position you spend your day in. Something as simple as sitting up straight and using proper ergonomics is good for your body, and that doesn't take much time at all.

Work out during your lunch break. Take a walk and eat as you walk. If there's a gym nearby, walk on the treadmill before work, during a break or before you jump in the car to go on to the next part of your day. Again, it's not about sweating or getting in shape for a marathon. It's about finding a way to get in some physical activity to make your body healthier and stronger. Exercise is a part of that balance. The pandemic restrictions taught us that you don't have to be sitting at your desk to work. You could make a call while walking, dictate a message or make notes on your phone, etc.

Find Your Strong: Learn to Ditch the Excuses!

Cramming your weekends as full of exercise as you can and then not doing anything good for yourself the rest of the week does not achieve the results you want. Three 10-minute blocks of exercise in a week's time can be very effective in building muscle and burning fat.

Think about the life balance you want between your work and leisure time and the time with family and friends. Balance out the time you spend at your desk with the time you spend moving around. Keep up your energy and keep up your health with some exercise, no matter how you earn your paycheck. If you are not moving and building muscle, you will not win the calorie-burning battle and you will not see the fitness gains you seek.

"I can't go to the gym. I'm not in good enough shape."

Read that headline out loud. Sounds silly, doesn't it? Going to the gym is about *getting* in shape, not necessarily *being* in shape. If you're not comfortable in a spandex unitard, don't wear one. You can get just as good of a workout in sweatpants and a baggy T-shirt. It doesn't matter if your hair won't go into a perfect bouncy ponytail. It doesn't matter if you don't have fancy clean shoes. It doesn't matter if there's a little roll above your sports bra. What does matter is that you're doing something good for you and your body.

Working out doesn't have to be anything fancy. Just make sure you've got a good pair of shoes (buy shoes for your activity; otherwise, use cross-trainers) and clothes you can move in. The beautiful part of gyms is that people are so sweaty and focused on their own exercise they don't have time to worry about what other people are doing or what they look like. Don't worry about being the only one who sweats or messes up in aerobics class or has a few extra pounds. Everyone has felt that way at one time or another. Once you've really hit the groove in your workouts, you will look and feel better, you will be less self-conscious, and you will feel better seeing the improvements in your health. That's why you are working out in the first place!

Another example of not worrying what you look like is when you're hanging out with your kids. If you take them to the pool, put on your suit and jump in. If they're running around playing soccer, put on some shorts and play. They'll be so excited you're playing with them that they won't care what you look like. Make exercise about fun and not about what you look like. Maybe someday you'll feel okay about that spandex unitard—or not. Either way, it's okay.

"I get enough exercise during the day."

Do you? Before you claim that you walk miles throughout the course of your day, get a pedometer to find out how many miles you actually walk. If you spend the day lifting, carrying, bending and twisting, you get more exercise than most people. However, you're not getting a total body workout that includes stretching, toning and lifting. Maybe you need to do some quick cardio to meet your fitness goals. Find the one part of your body you're not working, then work it.

If you have the advantage of a physical lifestyle, you're ahead of many people, but don't depend on your everyday routine to replace your workout routine. If you were truly getting the workout you needed for an ideal body, you would have an ideal body. If you don't have that body, it means you have some work to do. Figure out what you are lacking and find exercises that will improve those areas. Then, start doing those exercises.

Normal daily activity isn't designed to tone, stretch and strengthen your body. In order to do that, you'll have to put some extra effort into it. This extra effort will give you the benefits of exercise and a healthy lifestyle, and you'll get the added benefits of more energy and stamina to do what you want to do.

The trick is to find an exercise that's totally different from your 9-to-5 job. If your job involves a lot of walking, you'll need to do something besides walking to get the added benefits. Try lifting weights or doing some resistance training. If you lift a lot of heavy objects during the day, concentrate on cardio to burn body fat. If your daily activity has you on your feet, try swimming or biking. Do something different than what you're doing and you'll get results that are different than what you are getting now.

"Exercise hurts."

If what you're doing is painful, stop doing it! Exercise may make you feel a little sore but it shouldn't hurt. Straining yourself hurts. Overdoing it hurts. Moving and exercising your body should make you feel good. Work yourself to the point where you can feel it, but stop before it hurts.

If you wake up the day after you start exercising and you're a little sore, that's a good thing. If you can feel your muscles, it means they did work they're not used to doing. Do some stretching and you should feel better as the day goes on. Do not stop your exercise routine. Get right back to your plan and work out using a different muscle group. You'll find that you feel a little less sore each time you work out. After a while, you will find you don't even notice any stiffness. You will have a sense of pride that you are pushing yourself to be better.

"No pain, no gain," is a ridiculous saying. Pushing yourself until it hurts is the quickest way to seriously injure yourself. You're certainly not going to keep up any sort of activity that hurts, and you shouldn't. You can get plenty of gain without any pain.

People can hurt themselves exercising. That's a sign they've gone too far or they don't have the proper workout exercises in their plan. It's just like any other activity you do. If you are hurting yourself while working out, you're doing something wrong. Being stiff is one thing, but feeling pain is not okay.

It's possible to get injured when you are doing your exercise routines, even if you're careful. If you do get injured, take a break with that particular muscle group, but don't stop working out. If you've twisted your ankle, continue to work your upper body until your ankle heals. If you've hurt your arm, lay off the upper-body exercises until your arm is healed.

Remember, if you are getting hurt while working out, it's time to back off with that particular routine, but you must keep up with some version of it. Use your E Fit platform with lighter bands and rehabilitate your injury while continuing your other muscle group routines.

A quick tip: Make sure you are giving your body time to recover before you work it again. One day you might work your abs, your legs the next, then your back, and so on. Remember, there is a difference between soreness and pain. You should feel your muscle soreness after a good workout and you should be able to go about your day without pain.

"Exercising is pointless.
I'm not a size 2. Why bother?"

Exercise isn't a magic bullet cure-all. By working out consistently, you will see gradual, steady results. You'll see fat starting to melt away. Muscles will start to show where you've never seen them before. You won't see results overnight; but a month or so after you start exercising, you may notice that your pants fit a little looser. You may find yourself able to lift an extra bag of groceries.

You will find other benefits from exercise. Remember, Rome was not built in a day. Each day, you get closer to completing your vision. Your body composition results will start to show slowly and you will build it up more every day. Take the time and stick to your routine. The results will come, I promise.

Reward yourself throughout your exercise journey. Set exercise goals and work toward achieving them. Decide how many times per week you will work out and for how long. Decide which routine you are going to do each day. Write your goals down and commit to them. If they are not written down, they are only dreams and easier to dismiss. Write them, share them with someone you trust and ask them to hold you accountable.

My husband and daughter have an app on their phones that tracks their workout routines. They get notices when each finishes his/her workout. If one of them has not registered a workout for the day, they text each other and say, "I haven't seen your workout results today. Get to the gym." They have a built-in accountability factor that pushes them to stay engaged in their health.

Remember to reward yourself (non-food) when you reach your goal. Keep improving and setting new goals. Make them a little tougher each time and keep rewarding yourself along the way. Eventually, you'll start seeing changes in your body and your overall health, and you'll see how your hard work has paid off.

Not everyone is cut out to be a size 2. It's entirely possible to be a strong and healthy size 12. The trick is to start where you are and work with what you have. Work toward what you want. If it's a reasonable goal for you to be a size 2, then go for it. However, don't get discouraged when you have to go through all the sizes between 12 and 2 to get there. It takes time and dedication. You can do it, so stick with it!

"Counting reps, keeping track of time… It's all too hard."

Then don't do it. Not everyone likes to count reps, time themselves, figure out how many calories they've burned, or track how many miles they've gone in an hour. That's just fine. You don't have to if you don't want to. It doesn't really matter.

If you love counting, tracking and figuring, then by all means do it. You'll have a ready-made progress chart and can use it to push yourself to the next level. If you hate counting, tracking and figuring, don't do it. The important thing is that you're working your body, mind and spirit.

Do what you can. Work with your talents. If you're not a number tracker, there's no reason to pretend to be one. Do the working out without working the math. Do a few muscle repetitions. Work out for a few minutes. Travel a few miles on your walk, run or bicycle. You'll get all the benefits of working out without having to track your activity. Just make sure you occasionally increase the intensity and don't let yourself slack. You'll know when your body is tired and it's time to end your routine. If you stick with your daily routines, you'll notice you're able to do a little more than you could before you started.

Working out regularly is what gives you meaningful results. You won't want to exercise if counting, tracking and figuring become work for you. Make your routines fun, not excessively hard and stressful.

"I don't like trying new exercises."

There are many exercises out there that can help you reach your goals. Any gym or community education catalog has a ton of different classes with variations too numerous to mention. There's an impressive assortment of machines in the cardio area of a gym. It can be intimidating. It may seem like you have to try everything but you don't. The point of exercise is that you're doing something to exert energy. As long as you make an effort to work your body, you can stick to just a few types of exercise. Pick what you like to do and do it.

Don't try a trendy new workout if you don't want to. If

you like to run or walk or lift weights, then do that. Don't worry when you hear about the new thing that everyone is doing. Some people love trying new types of exercise and changing their routine. That's what works for them. If you already know what works for you, stick to that.

Be sure to increase the intensity periodically so your body doesn't grow used to the same thing. With one routine, it's easy to let your body settle into a pattern and plateau. If you've been doing the same routine for a few weeks at the same speed for the same length of time and your body is starting to plateau, it's time to step it up. Increase the amount of time you work out, or increase your intensity level. Don't let your body settle into a routine that doesn't push you to improve.

As long as you're consistently working a little harder and surprising your body once in a while, you don't have to try every new thing. New exercises are great, and there's always a new trend. Keep consistently doing your exercises and you'll see results.

"I can't exercise because I'm chasing after kids all day."

Great! Chase the kids. Chase them around the yard or the park or the pool. They'll love it. Play tag, Marco Polo, or ride bikes with them. It's family fun and you're getting exercise. Your kids spend the day running around and playing. If they don't, you should get them started. Running and playing is the best thing you can do for yourself and them. You are having fun, so you don't feel like you're exercising, which in turn makes you play longer and harder. It's good for your kids to see you exercising and having fun. They'll see you getting in shape and having fun with them, and that will create lifelong memories. Remember, you are your child's first teacher.

Getting your kids used to an athletic lifestyle is one of the best gifts you can give them. They won't reach middle age and have to alter their lifestyle to include more activity. They'll already be used to running around and having fun as a form of exercise. They'll reach adulthood with a healthy lifestyle already in place. What a great gift to give them.

The other great part of this gift is that your kids will love spending extra time with you. Kids typically love playing with balls and running after them. They love jumping into pools and jumping on trampolines. You can do all those things with your kids (maybe skip the backflips on the trampoline, though). Shoot hoops, shag balls, volley some balls over a net or shoot some pucks. You will raise your heartrate and your children will thank you for the fun you had with them. Later in their lives, they'll thank you for the great lifestyle you taught them.

My kids loved it when I took them to the skate park or on bike rides. They loved helping me practice new fitness routines. I took them to hockey practice and walked around the rink while they skated. I took them along on fun runs. We had a great time together.

We also read books, watched movies and did homework together, but we were sure to have time to run around playing and having fun every day. When my first son was a few months old, my husband and I bought a stroller that hooked to the back of our bikes. He rode hundreds of miles in that stroller. Eventually, he rode his own bike. Early on in his life, he and his siblings learned how important moving was for a healthy lifestyle. I am proud to say that all my children are physically active as adults.

"I can't feel good until I feel like a better parent."

A healthy parent raises children who are confident, happy and healthy. The good news is that you can raise your children while taking care of yourself. A parent is their child's first teacher. If you take care of yourself physically, mentally and emotionally, you will be better equipped to raise your children and you will be teaching them skills that will allow them to live a more satisfying life.

My husband and I were scared to death as parents. We worried about raising them correctly and giving them a good set of morals and values. We wanted to teach them the difference between right and wrong and expose them to the right things. We wanted to provide the tools they needed to be productive members of society.

I am no parenting expert, but we were careful to do a few things with our children that I think would work with any child. The skills we taught them gave them a solid foundation and helped them be thinkers later on in their lives.

1. Expose your children to the world. Take them on field trips. Take them to the zoo. Take them to Grandma's house. Take them to all the places children like to go so you can bond with them in fun settings. Expose them to things they are likely to run across as teenagers and adults. Take them to other neighborhoods and let them see what others have or don't have; you'll

be surprised at what they notice. Take them to places where people have more or less money than you. Introduce them to people of different races. Expose them to life outside their current reality.

2. Talk to your children about global events. Chances are you have opinions about various things taking place in the world or about people who have made decisions you don't agree with. Exposure to different ways of life will give them more tools to make better decisions later in their lives. Use these events as teachable moments. They'll remember the lessons you teach them.

3. Try to find examples that show your children how good they really have it. Chances are they are always asking for something because everyone else has it. They probably don't have it, but help them to realize that.

4. Spend time with your children in a nursing home, in a homeless shelter or anywhere people are without resources. Talk to them about what they saw and learned. Show them that even though some people don't have everything they want, they can still find reasons to be happy and live the best life they can. Encourage your children to think about the things they have and the things they can do and stop obsessing over what they don't have or can't do. Not everyone has fancy stuff. Not everyone is faster or better than they are.

5. Be honest with your children so they will be honest with you. It may be hard, but be honest with them

about things that have happened in your life. Tell them why you made some of the decisions you did. If you're not proud of some of the things you've done, tell them about those, as well. Talk about what you did and what happened as a result of your behavior or decision. Being honest with your children is one way to encourage them to be honest with you. Use your discretion to determine how much to tell them and at what age you will share which events. Obviously, a very young child doesn't need to know the details of your wilder days, but an older child who's entering their wild phase may need to hear it. You faced consequences. Let the kids know consequences are real and can happen to them. You're the most important role model your kids have, so be sure to use that position to its full advantage.

6. Help them make decisions by helping them think through a situation. So many times, we want to tell our children what they should do. Teach them how to reason through their situation by weighing the pros and cons. They might surprise you with what they know and what they think about.

7. Let your children try things. Again, there's a limit to how far you should let them experiment, but it's important to let them try things on their own. If they want a tattoo, talk about it. Honestly consider it. You don't have to say yes, but don't reject it flat-out. Ask them why they want a tattoo. If it's a well thought-out, mature reason, consider it as such. If they just want a tattoo to be cool or because their friends have one,

Find Your Strong: Learn to Ditch the Excuses!

ask them to think a little harder about what having a tattoo means and how permanent it is. They need to learn how a decision made on the spur of the moment can affect them for the rest of their lives. If they still want a tattoo, let them get a temporary one and walk around for a few days. Maybe they will change their mind.

8. If they want something and you're not opposed to them having it, give them a chance to work toward earning it. They need to learn that having something they want is not always free. We know as adults that we have to work to get what we want. That's a good lesson for children as they grow up. They may not thank you now, but they will later.

9. Get them started with setting goals at an early age. There's probably something your child wants. Help her set a goal to get it. If a small child wants a new toy, tell her what she can do to earn it, then follow through. If an older child wants to get a car, help him understand what he needs to do to achieve his goal. This is a great opportunity to teach children the benefits of working hard toward something.

You might be asking yourself, "How do these points tie into my eating and exercising, and why is Natalie writing about them in this book?"

The world around us tells us that everyone has more and is in better shape. It says we should be looking out for ourselves and to heck with everyone else. It makes people think everything is easy and everyone else is doing it. We can eat anything we want without gaining weight if we just take this pill, etc.

Eventually, people start feeling inferior to those around them. Their thoughts become their reality. They stop taking care of themselves because they don't have what others have or aren't as good as those around them. They think they are a failure if they fail one time. They give up on themselves and quit trying. If someone tells them they are fat and without reasoning skills, they believe what they are told.

Some of you may have had parents who told you that you were no good. They made your decisions for you, so you never learned how to think for yourself. Maybe you were taught that you couldn't or shouldn't share your thoughts and feelings, so instead you learned to stuff everything inside of you. Now, you are in an unhealthy situation and you don't believe in yourself. You let others influence who you are. You want to take better care of yourself, but you have failed before and don't want to try again. You have started believing that everyone else is in better shape or doesn't need to work at being healthy.

Depression, anxiety and self-doubt have set in and you have slowly stopped taking care of yourself physically, mentally and emotionally. You have stopped setting goals and looking for ways to be the best version of yourself. Only YOU can change who you are.

It's time for you to take control of your life! Do your own thinking. You are the driver of your destiny. Set some goals to be healthy. Talk to someone who can support you. Be honest with yourself and realize others around you are struggling in their own lives. Once you realize you aren't the only one, you can stop making excuses and set a course to improve your life.

The information above is what we did for our children. We believed that if we taught our children to think for themselves and reason through information at a young age, there was a greater likelihood they would be better prepared to live their own healthy lifestyle. If you do the same, you may help your children avoid some of the traps you have fallen into. If nothing else, reviewing the points above may empower you to make needed changes in your life.

"I don't think I'm a good role model for my family."

Thinking, eating, exercising and taking care of ourselves are all skills our children will observe, learn and hopefully carry forward in their own adult lives if they see it modeled by you. I've seen overweight parents eating crappy foods in front of their children. They fill the cupboards with junk food and have no healthy foods or snacks in the refrigerator or pantry. They take their children to the local buffet where they watch people overeat the wrong kinds of food, or overeat in general.

Picture this: You are at the mall. Your kids smell their favorite treat and beg you for it. You tell them no, and they throw a fit. You give in and buy it for them just to prevent a bad scene. Here is where you must be the mean parent and say, "I will buy you a treat, but you have to pick something healthier or we will go home." You may have to listen to complaining and grumbling, but you did what you needed to do. You acted as a good role model.

You read earlier that if parents don't stay physically fit or eat healthy foods, their children have no positive role models. Parents don't realize how making poor nutrition and exercise decisions for themselves has a lasting effect on their health and their children.

If you are not physically active, it is less likely that your children will be active. If you tell them that the family is just big boned and not meant to be thin, you are not being a good role model. If you begin eating healthy and exercising and using the information you have read in this book, you and your family will reap the benefits. You may hear some grumbling and complaining, but the end result will be a healthier family. Who doesn't want that?

As the leader of the family, you will need to redefine how your family relates to food. You will need to buy healthy snacks, go to healthier restaurants and make healthier meals at home. Your children will likely complain at first because they are used to having access to all the junk; but eventually, they will stop complaining and they will learn how to eat the new foods which are better for them.

As children, my kids learned how to eat vegetables instead of chips. As adults, they clear the vegetable tray at family gatherings. Chips are still not a readily available choice. They learned as children that chips and other ready-to-eat snacks are processed food and full of unhealthy ingredients. They learned that fresh vegetables are better for them, so that is what they prefer to eat. Now, we are teaching our grandchildren.

Once in a while, you can still bring home the favorite snack. Earlier in this book, you read that it's okay to have an occasional snack or treat, but once in a while and not every day. As you know, I am the excuse buster. My solution to this problem is *Change yourself and the rest will follow.* You know what you need to do. Now. it's up to you to follow through and do it.

"Old habits die hard."

That's the easiest excuse of all. Just because you have a habit of coming home and hanging out online or in front of the TV doesn't mean you have to keep that up. You can see what you're doing to yourself. If you keep doing the same thing, you'll get the same results. If there was a safe and effective way to lose weight without changing your habits, I'd encourage it. But the plain truth is that diet and exercise are the only way to lose weight and keep it off. Change your habits. It will change your body. Over time, you won't miss your extra TV time.

Don't use an excuse to get lazy. Use an excuse to spur results. If your current lifestyle isn't getting you the results you want, you know what you need to do. Get started!

You don't have to start all at once. Pick a few things you want to change. If you can't do that, pick one thing. You won't get great dramatic results from small changes, but you'll get results. The small results will encourage you to make more small steps toward becoming healthier.

Start exercising during commercials. Better yet, take a half hour of TV time to go for a walk. I think it should be a rule that every household should have one treadmill for each TV. People would be in a lot better shape. Put the treadmill in front of the TV. Read a book while you're on the exercise bike. Use the internet to research new exercises you might like to try. Do some of your favorite things while you exercise.

Meet some of your online buddies at the park and go for a walk. There's nothing wrong with spending time on the activities you love. Yes, you'll have to give up some of your old habits. Yes, it will be hard for a while; but you'll make new habits which will yield new results. Your healthy habits will be better for your body. I guarantee you'll have new favorite activities and you won't miss your lazy, out-of-shape days. You know what your old habits have done to your body. Same habits, same body.

Try eliminating obstacles. If you're too tired at the end of the day to work out, work out at the beginning of the day. Bring your exercise stuff to work, change after work, and go to the gym before you go home. Record your favorite shows and watch them while you're exercising, or save them for the weekend when you have time for a workout *and* a TV marathon. Get a stability ball and use it instead of a computer chair. Find ways to make your exercise time and your hobby time the same.

"It's not me I'm worried about. It's my family."

If you can sneak healthy food into the house, you can sneak in exercise activities. This means you might have to do some activity that draws you children out of their current routine. It may be hard work, but trust me that your family will thank you for it while enjoying some quality time with you. As stated earlier, your family will enjoy having some time with you, and you will also get some physical activity. If you do this regularly, you'll get the results you want.

Start by limiting your family's TV and computer time. You already know you should do this, so do it. You don't have to be strict with charts and timers. Work into it naturally. One day, after watching a movie, suggest that the whole family ride bikes around the block. The next day, get out some soccer balls and suggest a game in the backyard. The possibilities are endless—parks, basketball, Frisbee or whatever you think your family might like. Suggest activities and make them fun so that everyone wants to participate.

There are many ways to convince your family to get up and move. Start a little tournament or competition horse game on the basketball court. Invest in headphones and encourage the family to listen to their favorite music while they play.

Many gyms have family memberships. Try investing in one and go for an open swim a few nights a week or enroll the kids in a day camp. They'll learn some great teamwork skills and get the benefits of exercise and being in shape. Healthy kids are more likely to grow into healthy adults, so take advantage of your opportunity to get your kids off the couch and into activity.

It's not too late to change yourself or your family's activity level. You can't make them change, but you can help them explore ways to stay healthy, happy, lean and strong. Once your family gets into the habit of being active, they'll reap the benefits of a healthy body and they'll be thankful for that.

"I have a bad back/knees/neck/ankles/whatever."

If this is your case, certain kinds of exercise are off limits to you, but not all kinds. Talk to your doctor or a physical therapist. If they aren't any help, try a few personal trainer sessions. Get some expert advice on how to get started. Explain to the expert what makes your condition worse. They'll be able to get you started with activities you can do.

There has to be some part of your body you can move without hurting yourself. Work that one just a little bit. Take a walk around the block. Try some stretching. Do targeted weight lifting, tai chi, yoga, water aerobics or any gentle movement activity. Just because you have an injured body part doesn't mean you shouldn't experience all the benefits of exercise.

My husband's uncle is 87 years old and has a partial lung. He was struggling to live without his oxygen and had to use it all the time. He had an artificial knee and hip, and plates and screws in his back. He got tired of being sick and tired, so he made a decision to work out 10 minutes in the morning and 10 minutes in the evening. After a month of this routine, he was able to stop using his oxygen tank and was able to get back to doing some of the things he loved to do. An added benefit was that he no longer needed his oxygen tank.

A nagging injury or two doesn't mean you have to jeopardize your heart, arteries and muscles by depriving them of exercise. Being physically active, even for a few minutes a day, will benefit your body. You'll feel better even if you can't cure old injuries or pains, not to mention you'll look better and your mental state will likely improve.

If you're used to feeling pain and you've been sitting around because you don't feel like you can do anything, there is a good chance you've settled into sedentary habits and have probably put on some weight. Losing the extra weight will help you feel better. It'll take the stress off your joints. It's easier to move your body when there's less of it to move. Make yourself feel as good as you can. You may have been feeling bad for years. You don't deserve that. You deserve to feel as good as people who can move and enjoy their favorite activities.

"I'm still trying to lose my baby weight, and my baby is graduating."

No matter what stage of motherhood you're in (pregnant, new mom, mother of multiples, running carpools), taking care of yourself is the best way to take care of your children— from setting a good example to being someone your children are proud of.

If you're pregnant, you may obviously have to scale back your fitness routine. Talk to your doctor. Monitor your heart rate. Don't overdo it. If you're not feeling well, listen to your body and tone it down.

Being pregnant is not an excuse for not taking care of yourself. Yes, officially you are eating for two, but it doesn't mean you should consume useless calories and not have an exercise routine. Satisfy your cravings, then do some physical activity to burn off some of what you ate.

On the day our first son was born, I taught a one-hour aerobics class, walked two miles with my husband and mowed the lawn with our push mower. I could have sat around and complained that my back was killing me and my ankles were swollen, but I chose to have a positive outlook and forced myself to move. Later that day, I gave birth to a 10-pound, 5-ounce baby boy.

There are women like me who keep doing exercise classes until the day they give birth. Once the baby is born, they get going again by the time the baby is a week old. If your doctor and your body are okay with this type of activity level, then do it. However, if you're not approved to go "all out" during your pregnancy, by all means don't.

Every woman and every pregnancy is different. Don't compare yourself to me or anybody else, for that matter. Do the best you can do. Just make sure you're doing something.

Many pregnant women do a great job taking care of themselves. They're always aware of how they're treating their body. They work to ensure they get the right nutrition and sleep. Some work to get the proper exercise. Most pregnant women will, without exception, try to do the right thing for their unborn baby. As a pregnant mom, you are caring for the person growing inside you.

Young or old, single or married, parent or not, there is a special little someone who needs you to take care of yourself and live like that person would want you to live. Your unborn baby deserves it and so do you.

You want your child to be healthy and have every opportunity your fitness can give them. Take care of yourself so you can be ready for the challenges of being a new mother.

"I don't think I've put on any weight over the years."

The cold, hard truth is that unless you actively work to maintain your weight and your body, this probably isn't true. You might be one of the exceptions to this rule. Maybe your overall weight hasn't changed, but have certain areas changed or the way your body stores weight? Before you use this excuse, take a hard look at the facts. Do you find yourself hiding behind baggy clothes? Does your driver's license reflect an accurate weight? Do you even wear a swimsuit anymore? Could you get into the pants you wore a few years ago? Do you have the same type of stamina you did as a younger person? Do things sag where you don't want them to?

If you examine your answers to these questions, chances are that at least one of them is a no. Work on that. You may never again look like you did in your graduation pictures or wedding pictures, but that doesn't mean you should give up. Middle-aged spread happens, but you don't have to go down without a fight. Create a healthy body by carrying out your wellness plan.

As you age, your maximum recommended heart rate goes down. You have to be a little more careful with what you do. This doesn't just apply to exercise. You have to be more careful with a lot of things you do. Find your ideal heart rate for your age and work toward that. If you don't know what that rate is, do some research or consult your physician.

If you haven't stopped doing other activities you enjoyed when you were younger, exercise should be no different. A lot of exercises are especially well suited for people as they grow older. Try biking or water sports to minimize joint pain. Walk with your friends instead of jogging. Build your muscle stamina by using resistance tubes. You can still exercise; just do it differently. Don't punish yourself by not taking care of yourself just because you've aged a few years.

"I love my body the way it is."

Fantastic! You should, but don't tell me you don't have room for improvement. Is it toned where you want it toned? Does it sag in places you don't want sagging? Is your posture good? Do you hunch over your desk and carry that same form as you get up and walk to the copy machine? If you answered yes to any of these questions, you can work on improving your health.

Get to a point where you love seeing yourself as happy, healthy, lean and strong. Love the skin you're in, even if you don't look like a magazine cover model and you're carrying a few extra pounds; but never stop working to improve what you have. This is the body you've been given. Beating yourself up over it won't solve anything or make it all better. It won't make you healthier. It certainly won't make you happier, and it won't make you a better person. It will just make you a person with body issues, and the world does not need more of "those" people.

Take that body you love and use it. You've got a great opportunity to work it into shape. Get it out there and make sure it's as fit and toned as it can be. You'll feel even better about your body after you see what it can do. You'll have amazing adventures and great stories to share with those you love. The great thing about you is that you're unique and can work out in your own unique way.

Try something that makes you sweat, whether it's running, walking, biking or rock climbing. Try something you didn't know you could do. Master a difficult Pilates session or learn to swim. Don't want to do it alone? Help your friends love their bodies with a group exercise class or join a new running/walking/biking club. You'll be more grateful for what God has given you when you've seen how you can help create what you want for your body and your life.

I recently spent six months in an active 55+ resort. People there were living! They played pickleball, tennis, did water aerobics and wet cycling. Others played shuffle board and horseshoes. The park also had seven softball teams, and the minimum age for one team was 70. When I asked park residents how long they had been doing these activities, many of them indicated they started when they moved into the park because a friend encouraged them to try it. It is never too late to take care of yourself.

Loving your body doesn't mean accepting it as it is. Learn what your body can do, then do it. Over time, see if you can do a little more. Even if you're not in your ideal body or at your perfect age, love what you have while you're working on what you want.

"My friends cause me to self-destruct."

When you were young, you probably learned (or heard) that peer pressure is one of the main reasons people do stupid things. The same thing may be true when you get older. It's tough to admit you need to change, and it's tougher if you're not getting much support from your friends.

If you've been abusing your body by not working it or filling it with junk foods and thinking it was okay, you probably have a group of friends (or family) who think the same way you do. It's time for some changes. Try convincing your friends to change with you. Start by going for a walk or joining a gym together. If you're a little more ambitious than your friends, start a team and join a league for your favorite activity. If that doesn't work, change your habits without them.

You're strong enough to make changes by yourself. Tell yourself you're a person of great inner strength. You've already changed your eating habits, so you have proven to yourself that you have great strength and will power. Apply those skills to create a new workout regimen.

If you commit yourself to a new plan, you'll probably spend more time doing it. The good thing about spending time doing something you like is that it's likely you'll meet other people who are doing the same things. You will gain friends who support your new way of life.

If you're at the park every day, talk to other people you see there. Ask if they want to get together the next time you exercise. Take a class and start a conversation with people in the class. If you don't immediately gel with a fitness community, find a new one. Despite how it may seem, not all healthy people were born that way. They are probably like you. They are looking for friends who have the same interest.

I have a group of friends with whom I love being active. We have become true friends over the years. We call ourselves the Fit Chicks. We all learned that we like taking care of our health. We go on mini retreats every summer. We eat healthy, exercise, talk about life and laugh a lot (great for mental health). We plan our menus and start each day with a workout. Every day, we plan for some other form of physical activity (canoeing, hiking, biking, horseback riding, white water rafting). You can do the same thing.

You don't have to ditch all your friends. If your friends are extremely destructive and cause you to fall back into your old health habits, though, you may need to stop spending so much time with them. If you're able to maintain your new health habits and keep your friends, by all means don't ditch them. They may eventually join your new lifestyle when they see the benefits you are gaining by taking care of yourself.

If they refuse to join you in your attempt to get healthier, try to sabotage your new lifestyle, make you feel bad about it or try to make you stop living your new life, it may be time for new friends. Don't let other people stop you from being the person you want to be. Your friends can either motivate you or demotivate you. Your friends can slow your progress or speed it up.

Be sure to pick friends who allow you to work on improving yourself and will encourage you to be better. If you have to, say to your friends, "I'm making some changes in my life. I'm surrounding myself with positive things and positive people. Please help me by being one of my positive people." Talk to them about what you're learning about being happy. Invite them to read books or watch motivational media with you.

Seek positive people and you will find positive people. Your positivity may rub off on your friends. They may become more positive, which will make them a better person for you to be around. If everyone around you is working to be better, you will all get the benefits of being healthier.

If your family is causing you to self-destruct, that's a little harder. Although you can basically choose your friends, you are more or less stuck with the family you have. Your inner strength is important here. Force yourself to do healthy things when you are together, and maybe they'll start. Reach out to supportive, healthy family members for encouragement. Make plans with them to have healthy alternatives at family functions. Walk or do some type of physical activity after the family has finished eating.

Our families have healthy food at our functions. We make salads, have fresh veggies, eat less bread, and almost always have some sort of fruit to snack on as an alternative to chips and dip. This ensures we will balance the delicious, smaller portioned desserts at the end of our meals.

"I don't like getting up at 5:00 am."

Who said anything about 5:00 am? Many people like to get up and get their workout done first thing in the morning, but it's not for everyone. There are advantages to getting up early, though. It's not as hot, it won't be as busy, it's quiet and might be a good time to clear your head before facing the day. Don't worry about the "right time" and the "right way" to work out. There are conflicting articles everywhere about the perfect time to work out; but they do tend to agree on the fact that you need to exercise. Do it your own way in your own time.

The most important thing about exercise is finding a time that works for you and scheduling it into your day like any other "to do" activity. Look at your day and find the time you can (and will) exercise. It might be 5:00 am, while your children are napping, during your lunch break or right after dinner. The most important thing is to schedule it.

Research shows that once you've written something

down and committed to it, you are very likely to do it. You wouldn't break an appointment with someone else unless there was an extreme reason, so don't miss an appointment with yourself. You live with your body. Take the time to treat it right.

"It's too cold/hot."

I live in Minnesota. It gets cold here. I know about this excuse. I also know about the sluggish feeling I can get when I'm cooped up all day sitting inside looking out at the gray sky. It's easy to camp out on the couch and eat comfort foods, drift in and out of a nap and basically do nothing all day.

One day of laziness is fine every once in a while; but if you're stuck in a cold snap, it's likely to be several days in a row. It's not so easy to get back to your routine the next day. Remember, you should have your exercise scheduled into your day like any other event. You don't skip other important events in your day because it's too cold or too hot. Besides, if you are laying around because of the weather, you are likely to get bored and eat more junk food, which will compound your problem. You are not exercising *and* you are adding more useless calories to your food intake. Think how much easier it would be if you stopped using the weather as an easy excuse.

It does take a little creativity on your part if you don't like being outside during these temperatures. Your gym is open. Your local community center or school might have an open gym that you can take advantage of. Most malls are heated (or air conditioned) and allow people to come in and walk laps.

If you can't leave the house, you don't have to be a slug all day. Run up and down the stairs a few times. Build a fort with the kids and have an in-home adventure. March in place.

Pull out your E Fit platform and do one of my 10-minute routines. You don't have to do a huge workout if you're truly stuck in the house. Making the effort to get in a little activity will make you feel better and look better. Besides, if you are stuck in the house, you would be hard pressed to convince me that you couldn't find 10 minutes in your day to be physically active.

"Okay, so what do I do?"

Now, it's time to get started. You know you should. Below are a few tips.

First, make a plan. Talk to your doctor and come up with an activity plan that's reasonable for you. Keep your goals in mind when you make your plan. If you want to increase your stamina, be sure to plan enough cardio. If you want increased strength, concentrate on strength training. Be sure to set an ambitious enough schedule so you can meet your goals.

Don't overdo it at first. Work into your routine slowly. If you're used to a routine of walking from the couch to the fridge, don't expect to run a mile the first day. Plan to work out three times a week for about 20 minutes a day at first. Gradually increase this routine until you are working out five times a week for at least 30-45 minutes a day. You can do it, just not all at once.

Get others involved. You'll have an easier time sticking to your routine if you have people who hold you accountable.

Get a buddy who will wake you up or meet you at the gym or play a game with you. It's more fun to do activities with other people. You may even have such a great time you'll forget you're improving your body.

As I mentioned earlier, my husband and our daughter have an app on their watches that shows each other's fitness activity for the day. They call or text each other if they don't see workout results posted on their watches by 6:00 pm every day. They push each other and rib each other until the lagging one moves to register his/her workout. You can do the same. Find a workout partner who will hold you accountable and get active.

Celebrate your victories. When you're able to run faster than before, celebrate. When you make it through your aerobics class without feeling like you're going to die, celebrate. When you wear smaller pants for the first time, celebrate. If you meet your workout goal for the week, celebrate. Recognize what you can do with your beautiful body and do it. Celebrate every step of the way!

Training Your Mind

The most common roadblock to getting a fit body is winning the mental battle that rages within our heads. You're afraid and don't think you can do it, so you don't fully commit to your plan. Once your mind is in shape, your body will get on board. It's a matter of loving yourself and working to be your best self. If your mind is flabby and out of shape, your body will not have a chance. Your mind must motivate your body to get up and move. Be the boss over your mind.

Getting your body in shape can be as simple as telling yourself to make a few changes to your diet and exercise regimen. These changes will be good for your mental health. It takes a little extra work to get a fit mind, but the extra work is definitely worth it. It's no fun to have a healthy body that feels good if you don't have a healthy mind to enjoy it. A healthy life will go a long way toward helping you get mentally fit, but it's not the whole solution.

Setting goals and achieving them is a mental process which requires thought, planning and insight. Being mentally strong will help you achieve goals, feel better about yourself and help you live to your full potential. A more fit mind will make you sharper at work, capable of better decisions and allow you to be a better role model for those around you.

Good mental fitness allows you to have the life you want. Good mental health means you can enjoy life and take advantage of opportunities as they present themselves to you. It means you are more prepared for whatever happens to you or around you. It will give you the confidence, attitude and clarity you need to get through life. We have discussed healthy eating and physical activity, so let's see if we can improve your mind, as well. Let's examine excuses people use to avoid working toward a healthier mind. Then, we'll examine why it's so important to overcome these excuses.

"I never get what I want."

The fastest way to get what you want is to set a goal. Once you decide what you want, have a clear goal and a clear plan to get it. This takes work and time, but you can do it. You may not get everything all at once, but by setting goals and working toward them you can eventually find your level of desired success.

Setting a goal can seem intimidating, but it simply means deciding what you want and how you're going to get it. If you've never had a focused plan for achieving an outcome, it was probably unsuccessful. You can't do the same thing over and over and expect different results. It's time to try something new.

Setting goals helps you decide on new behaviors you will

adopt to improve your overall health. Goals help you focus on what is important to you, and reviewing them on a regular basis helps you maintain focus and keeps you moving forward. When you accomplish your goals, you will have reason to celebrate your success. You will be able to see where you started, where you ended and how you will accomplish your next goal.

You can set a goal to achieve anything. The important thing is to make a goal, not just dream about something you want. Goals have action steps and a deadline. Setting a goal means you're committed to working toward getting the results you desire. It means you're willing to put in some effort to get results.

Let's say you want to set a weight-loss goal, which is fairly common for Americans. The first step is to define exactly how much weight you want to lose. Next, define how much time it would take to reach your desired weight. For example, you might set a goal to lose two pounds a week for a month. Pick a date a month from now. Subtract eight pounds from your current weight. Write down what you will weigh in one month, then commit yourself to reaching that weight on that date.

Never take your eyes off that goal. Take action toward your goal every day. If you don't reach the desired level of performance along the way, it's not a big deal—you have a month. Don't give up and quit. Dig in and work harder. Weigh yourself on your goal date. If you've really committed yourself to your goal, you'll see the number you want.

Setting healthy living goals is a transferable skill. Setting a fitness goal involves the same steps as setting a goal to buy a home, finishing a scrapbook project, getting married or saving for retirement. There's nothing you can't do if you set a goal. That's how people achieve important things in their lives.

Start today. Set a goal. Any goal. Make it an easy goal and one you know you can achieve. Reaching this goal will help you build the confidence that you can do it again. Once you see how good it feels to set and achieve a goal, you won't want to stop. You'll find that you have what you want, and you will know how to get what you want in the future.

"I've set goals and they've never come true."

Most people don't write down their goals. That's a big part of why they don't achieve them. It's easy to have a goal in your head, but writing it down is one of the most important steps. Writing down your goal gives you a specific record of what you want to achieve. It makes you accountable to doing what you've said you will do. It gives you a visual way to track your progress. Writing down your goal means that *you can't change it*. If you stop working toward your goal, you have given up.

Let's review why setting and writing down goals is so important:

1. It makes it clear in your head. Your goal is for you. Others may assist you in reaching your goal, but it's really what you want, not what they want. When you write your goal, you create a focus point with a deadline and a plan for how you are going to get there.

2. Writing down your goals allows you to clearly state

what you specifically want to achieve. You define individual steps you are going to take to find your success, not just general statements (*I want to lose two pounds a week for four weeks for a total of eight pounds lost*).

3. Scientific studies show that the likelihood of realizing your goal increases when you write it down.

4. Writing down your goals helps you focus on what you really want. Stand at your window and look out at a lake. You see the water, the trees on the other side of the lake and the couple who are fishing. You see something on the other side of the lake that you can't quite identify, so you grab your binoculars. You see the object better, but not perfectly, so you focus more. Suddenly, you have a clear view of what you wanted to see. Writing our goals down allows you to focus on what you really want to achieve.

5. There is much information on goal writing that says writing down what you want to achieve will become embedded in your mind. A specific part of your brain engages, which allows you to have greater success.

No more excuses! Grab some paper, a pen and a glass of your favorite beverage. Write down what you want to achieve. Be specific. What *exactly* do you want to achieve, what steps are you going to take, and when do you want to reach the goal?

Once you've written your goal, post it somewhere where you will see it every day. Put it on your fridge so you can see it when reaching for a snack that could sabotage your goal. Put it on a sticky note on your desk so you see it before you run to the candy machine. Stick it to the bathroom mirror so you think about it every morning as you prepare for your day. Write your goal in your journal (or blog, or whatever). Write it everywhere. It doesn't matter what your goal is or how long- or short-term it is. Just keep a record of it. Think about it every day and what you'll do to help you achieve it.

It's also important to share your goal. Tell a few people you trust and who you know will support your efforts. Ask them to keep you accountable to your goal and ask them to help you reach it. Share why you've chosen to set the goal and why it's important to you. Share how you will celebrate your goal once you've achieved it. People who love you will want to help you work toward a celebration (especially if they can party, too). Let other people know what you're planning and why it's important to you.

Define your action steps. What activities will you do every day to reach your goal? How will you measure your progress? What tools will you use to make your goal a reality? Who will help you? Write it all down. Look at your plan every morning. Think about what you will do today to get closer to achieving it, then be sure to do it. If you need to write down a step-by-step activity list for each day, do it. If completing your list for the day is your victory, celebrate that.

Now that you have a goal and a plan, all you need is a reward. What will you give yourself when you reach the goal? Obviously, if you're setting a fitness goal, a food reward would be counterproductive. Maybe reward yourself with some new jeans. Take yourself to a movie. Spend the afternoon with the kids in the park doing nothing. Pick a reward that's meaningful to you, but make it proportional to the goal. Maybe you can set a weekly goal for one new item. If it's a long-term goal, give yourself a larger reward—a shopping spree, a vacation, hiring a maid, or whatever makes sense to you.

Look at the plan you've made and stick to it. Evaluate it periodically. If the plan you originally set isn't moving you toward your goal within the timeline you've set, adjust the plan. If you're committed to your goal and your reward, you'll be willing to work a bit harder to get the end result. If that still doesn't work, adjust your goal. It's okay to change your goal. It's okay to be realistic with yourself. When you set your next goal, make it a little more challenging.

If you've never set a goal before, it's hard to know exactly what's involved, so make it a learning experience. It's okay to consider a goal achieved if you worked your plan every day as hard as possible. The important thing is to keep your eyes on the prize, not only the reward you'll give yourself, but the reward of a healthier, happier and leaner body.

Fully commit yourself to your goal. Be honest with yourself. Are you really working toward your goal? Commitment is the most important part of reaching a goal. Commit, work at it and NEVER give up!

"People make fun of my goals."

It's hard for people to change. It may be hard for you to change into a goal-setting person and it may be hard for other people to suddenly start seeing you as one. They may devalue your goal because they think it's too hard. They think you can't achieve goals, they don't think goal-setting works, they don't believe in you or they don't believe in themselves. It could be something as simple as them wanting the same thing as you and not knowing how to get it. It's definitely easier to reach your goals with help and support from other people, but remember that your goals are for you.

Goals can be crushed by other people's reactions. Tell people why your goal is important. Tell them how your goal will help you with what is missing from your life. Tell them about the work you've already put into achieving your goal and the steps you've planned. Tell them about the reward you've planned for yourself. Tell them this is what you've chosen to do and that you would like their support. If they aren't willing to give it to you, let them know they'll miss out on something important to you. Tell them you'd love to have them as a goal buddy. If they still don't believe in you, let it go. Let them see the end result after you've achieved your goal.

The bottom line is to not let your goals be dependent on other people. You can't control what other people will do or say or how they'll react. Take charge of yourself and your own life. It all comes down to you.

"I don't know what I want."

It can be tricky to figure out what you really want. There can be many things and it's hard to pick just one. You may even work toward something and find it's really not what you wanted at all. It's okay to try different things to see what sticks, to be confused about life or to set a goal. In the end, you'll have something you are willing to work toward. It's also important to not bite off more than you can chew. If you set several goals for several different objectives, it's hard to keep up with working all the plans. Set one or two goals that don't conflict with each other. Work on them, achieve them and celebrate them when they are accomplished. Then, you can set another goal. Success breeds success.

If you can't think of something you want, start with something you don't want. If you're unhappy with something currently happening in your life, set a goal to change it. If something is about to happen that you don't want, set a goal to prevent it.

Let's say you're unhappy with work. What can you do to make it better? Do you need to get a new degree, work for a different company, make more money, quit working full-time or start interviewing to see what the options are? Set a goal to change your situation. Get creative or even a little crazy.

Make sure your goal addresses your problem. If you don't like the company culture, set a goal to meet a few new people. With your new friends, you may find work more bearable. If you hate the company but love the work you do, set a goal to look for a new job. Even if you can't find a job you would like, the process of seeing what's out there may help you realize that your job isn't that bad. Sometimes, setting a goal to follow a process is just what you need. A process goal will sometimes result in change or it may result in learning something new. Either way, you'll have achieved something.

If you purchased this book, it probably means that you want to achieve some healthy lifestyle goals. Start there. If you're tired of being a plus size, work toward a specific size. Start with a goal to eat right for one week. Specifically define what eating right means to you. *I will eat five servings of fruits and veggies daily. I will keep a food journal every day for a week. I will switch from whole milk to skim.* Whatever it is, be specific so it can be measured. Write down your goal and work toward it. If you set a short-term goal, it's okay to set the same goal for a few weeks in a row.

When you consistently reach that goal and it becomes part of your life, go ahead and set a new goal. Setting a series of short-term goals will get you the same results as setting one long-term goal. Find what works for you and go for it!

"I don't know how to set goals."

Commit to a goal. There are steps that can help you meet your goal, but setting it and committing to it are the most important.

How to set a goal:

1. Decide what you want and be specific. Don't set a goal to lose weight. Set a goal to lose 20 pounds by your birthday. Set a goal to eat five servings of fruits and veggies a day for the next month. Set a goal to walk for half an hour each night. Setting specific goals means you will know when you've achieved them. Setting a deadline tells you how long you have to work toward achieving them. Make sure you can measure your goals. Use a scale, a journal, a chart with stickers or whatever it takes to make you successful.

2. Make sure your goals are realistic. If you hate getting up in the morning, don't set a goal to get up and run at 5:00 am every day. You can get the same effect from

running after work. Set goals that are achievable. You won't lose 10 pounds in one week, but you can lose two pounds in a week. Set a goal to lose two pounds every week for 10 weeks. Make the goals challenging, but make them something you can realistically do. If you set your goals impossibly high, you'll get discouraged when you don't have the superhuman ability to reach them.

3. Write down your goals. Include the measurement you want to achieve and the deadline to get them done. Post your goals where you can see them during the day. Remember, if you don't write down your goals, you won't be as committed to them. Writing them down gets them in your mind to achieve specific things. Write them in your diary or in your blog, hang them on the fridge, put them on your calendar every day or whatever works for you. It's also a good idea to share your goals with other people so they can support you.

4. Break your goals down into small, achievable steps. If your goal is to eat five servings of fruits and veggies a day, make a list of what you will eat with each meal and snack. Then, make sure you have enough fruits and vegetables in the house, ready to eat when you are hungry. Wash them when you get home so you can readily pick one up and bite into it. Breaking it into steps makes your goal easier to achieve because you know what you need to do. Little steps can make big changes.

5. Start at step one. Do what's on your list at a time you

Find Your Strong: Learn to Ditch the Excuses!

are ready to do it. Stick to your list. If you get off track, get right back on track with the next step. One misstep doesn't mean your goal is impossible, unachievable or stalled. It might take longer to achieve, but you can still do it.

6. Celebrate when you have achieved your goal and celebrate your progress. Set specific celebrations within your goal. Lose five pounds and get a pedicure. Get a better job, then take your family out for dinner. The reward you set will be secondary to the benefit of your goal, but you'll realize it feels just as good. Even if you occasionally lose sight of your goal when the going gets tough, keep your eye on the reward.

7. After you achieve your goal, continue to move forward by setting a new goal. Once you see how well your first step in goal-setting goes, you'll want to get those results in other areas of your life. Repeat the above steps. You'll see that your goals keep getting bigger and that you keep achieving them. You will learn what success feels like.

"If I have _____, I'll be better."

Fill in the blank. You can only build yourself for so long on what other people think before you start to feel empty. What's important to other people may not (or should not) matter to you. Build your life on what YOU want. If you're not living your ideal life right now, don't try to convince yourself that you have it or need it. Even if you seem like you have it all, it may not mean you do.

When I was in high school, I was the golden girl. I had good grades, was a good athlete, had plenty of friends and a loving family; but I still craved the approval of the local golden boy. In the end, his approval didn't get me anything except being obsessed with my body, alienated from everyone I knew and striving to be even more "perfect" than I already was. All it got me was misery and the desire to get out of town and away from those I loved.

After time (and therapy), I learned to be confident and realized that what I had was already great. I didn't need the approval of someone else to make me happy. Once I had that figured out, I was able to change things in my life that allowed me to live the way I wanted to—not how others thought I should.

The secret is to have what *you* want, not what everyone else wants for themselves or for you. A little scrutiny can help you feel better about your life if you take the time to reflect on it. I challenge you to look around and ponder how many people would want what you already have.

The grass always looks greener on the other side of the fence. Look at what you already have in your life. Try to remember how much you wanted what you have and how hard you worked to get it. Ask yourself why you wanted it in the first place. Was it to impress those around you or because you really wanted it? If something in your life doesn't serve a purpose for you, get rid of it.

If the desire to have something no longer applies, evaluate the situation and change it. Set a goal to achieve your new desire. You may not have to change everything you're already doing. Maybe you just need small tweaks. Ask yourself why you want something. If it's for your benefit and not on someone else's behalf, then go out and get it.

You may find yourself jealous of others and what they have. It must have been important to them, so they found a way to get it. You can do the same thing. Think about the true reason you want what they have and think about why you don't have it, then decide what you can do to change your situation. Set a goal to get what you want—not what other people have. It has been said that envy is the root of all evil. I would agree.

In this country, people often envy money, so I'll use that as an example. If you don't have money, think about why. Is it because you have a job you love but doesn't pay as well as other jobs? Is it because you don't have the skills you need to get the job you want? Is it because you've chosen to be more about family than work?

If you had more money, what would change? Would you change your house, your car, vacation plans, your children's education savings? Are those things important to you, or do you just want them because others have them? What would you give up to get them? Nothing in life is free. You almost always need to give something up to get something you want.

Jealousy can drive us to go after things we don't want or need. We think we would be better off if we had what somebody else has. The reason we want something may not even be valid to our situation. The cost of getting it might be greater than the reward.

If what others have is important to you, set a goal and get after it. Don't sit around and complain how you don't have it as good as others. They made life happen and so can you!

"I have everything I want, so why should I change?"

I've never been able to achieve this level of success, so congratulations to you. Maybe it's time to ask yourself if you are just putting on a front to protect yourself. What's your secret dream you haven't achieved? Do you want to start your own business? Have you always wanted a pool with your house? Have you always wished you had a college degree? Do you really have a life you love, or have you settled because you think you can't achieve anything bigger?

If you have it all, ask yourself if you're any happier for it. If the answer is no, reflect on what currently fills your life, then fill it with what makes you happier. Having everything is probably an awesome feeling. Are you filling your true needs with random stuff so you look great from the outside? Having all the material things you want or having what everyone else wants does not mean you have everything you need.

Ask yourself what's missing from your life. What would it take to make you truly happy? What are you covering up? Are you substituting random stuff for an underlying issue that you need to address? People tend to use proxies such as food, drugs, alcohol or shopping to cover deeper issues. Rather than addressing those issues, people stuff themselves with unhealthy food or other substances. Time for you to rethink!

When I was growing up, everyone had to have the latest designer jeans. When I got mine, I thought I would be happier. I was happier for the moment, but the jeans didn't address the real issue I was facing, so the effect was short lived. I may have looked better, but I was still struggling mentally and emotionally. I needed to address the real issue before I could be happy and healthy. Having fancy jeans wasn't a life accomplishment. Looking cute wasn't something that made me feel good for very long.

Are you truly happier when you get your desired object, or are you covering something up? Reflect on what's happening in your life that makes you fill it with the wrong stuff. Find someone who can help you deal with the real issue so the stuff becomes less important to you.

Get to a point in your life where you feel good about who you are and not what you have. Yes, it's easier to buy designer jeans (or whatever it is that makes you feel good), but they won't really make you happy. You must deal with the real issue that causes your life to be unsettled. Once you do that, you'll be on track to live a happier, healthier and leaner life.

"I'm too depressed to take care of myself."

If you acknowledge to yourself or others that you're depressed, there is an issue you need to address. You need to do something right away. You cannot ignore depression. I would really encourage you to find professional help because depression is a serious issue.

When you are really depressed, it can be hard to focus on anything other than how bad you feel. Just getting out of bed can be a challenge, much less doing anything like taking care of yourself, your family, your house or other obligations. Staying in survival mode isn't going to make you any less depressed. As a matter of fact, it will likely compound your issues. It's okay to be sad and it's okay to have periods when you do nothing, but if you cannot change that feeling in a couple of days, it may be time to seek additional support.

The thing about depression is that it doesn't go away on its own. Unless you do something professionally, you'll likely stay depressed. This is one of those situations where you can't just set a goal to be happier. Seek medical or emotional support from a professional.

If it is not full-on depression, but you find yourself being sad and lethargic, go back to what you learned earlier. Set a goal to take little steps to care for yourself which will hopefully make you happier. It doesn't have to be one big goal. Set a small goal to get out of bed. Then add a shower and go to work.

A progressive goal allows you to find small successes along the way. Once you've met one goal, set another one. It might be to go outside and walk around the block or to feed your body healthy food. If you need to, set a goal to eat. Set a measurable goal to get better every day. It doesn't have to be all at once. Getting better one step at a time is valid, as long as you are working to get better.

When you're depressed, talk to someone. This might be the perfect time to lean on your goal buddy. Tell them how you feel. They may not understand, but the act of talking about your issues might make you feel better.

Here is an important piece of advice: Don't pick a goal buddy who's also depressed. You need someone who can help and support you, not commiserate with you. You need to be able to share your thoughts and feelings with them and ask them for feedback. They may tell you you're spending too much time in one area of your life and not enough time doing other things. Listen to them and make adjustments where you can. It may be hard, but it'll be even harder if you don't deal with your depression head on.

Depression is a serious issue and you may need a more serious intervention. Don't be afraid to reach out for help! *(National Suicide Prevention Number: 988)*

Talk to a psychiatrist, trainer, pastor, hotline worker, your best friend or whoever you are comfortable talking to. Make sure they are able to listen to you without judgment. If you feel like you have no one to talk to, start a journal or a blog. Have a place where you can acknowledge your feelings and begin to examine them. These writings could also be good information to share with your professional, as it will give some insight on how you are feeling, what is happening in your life to make you feel this way, and how often you are feeling depressed. Remember, it's okay to reach out to professionals who deal with depression.

"I don't know anyone who can help."

While it's never impossible to get your life on track, it's easier if you have a support system. Surround yourself with positive people who will help you reach your goals. If you don't already know these people, find them. Reach out to new people at work, at the gym, in the park, at school with your kids or at church. You can find understanding people wherever you are.

If you can't find positive people, surround yourself with positive things. Try listening to uplifting music or motivational speeches in your car. Read an inspirational book. Read the Bible. Get your hands on positive material and work to change your mind to a positive mindset. If you spend more time chasing good, more good will come your way.

A great place to search for positive material is your library. It's full of great books and audio materials you can use for free. It's also likely to be full of people who want to learn and people who are looking to improve themselves. If you're apprehensive, ask a librarian to help you find items you are looking for. They love to talk about books and materials and would love to help you. Tell them your goals and let them help you find resources.

Libraries are also places where various community groups meet or advertise their meetings. Your librarian may be able to point you toward a helpful group of people who have similar struggles as you. Find out if there are any motivational speakers in your area. Look for a referral hotline for people you need access. Resources are out there if you look for them.

When I was at my lowest point, I got my hands on all the inspirational materials I could find. It's amazing how you can change your mindset when you change what you put into your mind. The self-help industry is huge. You will find a book, an audio, a website or a YouTube video that can help you.

In my case, I knew that being sad was consuming my life, so I decided to give myself over to God. I asked Him for all the help He could give me. I promised Him that I would do my part to get healthy. I prayed and I filled myself with good information. I was able to overcome my eating disorder, get over my bad relationship and move on with my life. You can do it, too. It's okay to ask for help. You just need to seek it out!

"I'm too busy taking care of others."

The first thing a doctor will tell a patient is that they should take care of themselves. For stressed-out individuals, most doctors will prescribe that you take time to sleep, relax and recharge your batteries. Doctors will tell you to get exercise and move your body. If you're not seeing a doctor, prescribe these things for yourself. Take care of yourself as you would for others.

Taking care of yourself doesn't just mean eating right. Take time to recharge your batteries. Take care of yourself by eating healthy, getting plenty of rest and filling your mind with positive messages and thoughts. You'll be happier and you'll be a better caretaker for others.

If oxygen masks drop down on an airplane flight, the first thing you're supposed to do is put your own mask on, *then* help those around you. If you're unable to breathe, you won't be able to help other people. Don't feel guilty about saving yourself first. Be at your best for those you care for. You can do so much good for others when you operate at full capacity.

Caring for others is hard work. If you are tired and run down, you can become negative and bitter about helping others. This is not good for anyone. Get other people involved in your care routines. Tell them how you've been feeling and that you need help. Say something like, "I've been a little tired and depressed lately, so I could really use your support."

Sometimes, it's not about physically taking care of someone. You may have a friend, colleague or family member with a doom and gloom mentality. Their negativity may be wearing you out. Maybe you notice yourself becoming more negative as you spend time with them. Being around this kind of friend can make *you* feel depressed or negative along with them. You don't need that.

In my opinion, you have two options:

1. You can be super positive around them and hope it wears off so they change.
2. You can find a way to spend less time with them. Remember, the goal here is to take better care of yourself so *you* can be happy, healthy, lean and strong.

"I don't have time to work on my mind."

You use goal-setting skills to set body goals. You can do the same thing with your mind health. Write your journal that you are going to read inspirational books, listen to YouTube videos, podcasts or any other media form where you can find positive, motivating materials to help yourself think and feel better about yourself.

Your mind is just as important as your body, so you need to nurture it. Treat your mind well and it will treat you well for a long time. Plan this time in your day just like anything else that's important to you. My husband and I find time every day to listen to one of several favorite speakers who keep us motivated and thinking positively. The world loves to fill us with negative stuff like today's so-called news and politically challenging posts on social media.

If your mind is in shape, you'll have a better tool to take care of yourself. If your body is already in shape, good for you. You are halfway to being happy, healthy, lean and strong.

You can be in great physical shape, but it can be exhausting, depressing and downright draining if you are constantly fighting your thoughts. Being able to control how you think is very important. Your mind can easily sabotage you. Talk positively to yourself and have nice phrases to repeat to keep you from sliding into a space where you don't want to live.

Being mentally fit is as important as being physically fit. It's not an either/or proposition. Your body needs repetitive activity to stay strong and so does your mind. Being physically fit and not mentally fit only gives you half the benefit of total fitness. Try some new skills that will benefit your mind, which in the end will affect your body.

By now, you should be using goal-setting to get yourself in better physical shape. You can work on your mental health while you are walking, running, biking, skiing, boating, etc. Depending on your activity, you can add some form of positive media to your workout routine, thereby getting physically and mentally fit at the same time.

Another way you can work on your mental health is by using some of your gym or activity time to connect with other like-minded people. This is a great way to make new friends. As your mind gets stronger, you'll find yourself with renewed spirit to work on your body. As your body gets stronger, you'll have more energy, learn more and become more mentally strong. It's a win-win!

"I'm just too overwhelmed."

Take it one step at a time. Getting your act together and getting a healthy mind and body is a big deal. Getting up 15 minutes earlier to read an uplifting book is a small step. Taking a walk after dinner is a small step. Skipping dessert and eating fruit instead is a small step. Do one of those steps at a time. Master one step, then move on to another. Maybe you can't manage a major change in your life right now, but you may be able to handle a minor change.

Getting mentally and physically fit is a big process. You may need to give up some things that are less important to you at this moment. Being totally fit is important and it takes some resources. Don't give up your favorite things all at once. Remember small steps.

If you feel like you can give up some TV time, decide if you will stop watching a show completely or if you will record it. If you feel like you can give up lunch with your co-workers once a week, use that time to run errands and free up your nights. If you feel like you can give up fast food once a week, use that money to buy fitness equipment. Figure out the things you want, then look at what you're willing to do to get them. You'll always have time for what's important.

You burn about twice as many calories sitting up than laying down, and twice as much to stand up. Walking or moving around will burn twice more. If all you can do is sit up a little longer than you did yesterday, do it and celebrate it. Tomorrow, sit up a little longer. Next week, stand up. Little goals are the key. Walk around the block, then two blocks, then three blocks. You get the picture.

If the four-step program of nutrition, aerobics, training and service seems like too much, don't give up. Break them down into manageable steps.

Remember that the four components are equally

important in developing total fitness, but each piece represents just one set of small steps. You can do those. When you combine a few small steps from each area of the NATS (Nutrition, Activity, Training your mind, and Service) program, you'll get four times the benefits to live a happier, healthier, stronger and leaner life!

"I'm too out of control."

There are many areas of our lives we can't control. Look closely and find what you can control. The only thing you have any say over is yourself. Change a little at a time. Don't try to make yourself a completely different person overnight. Find one area in your life that can use some improvement and work on that. Over time, if you work on enough areas, you'll find you have more control.

Spend 10 minutes doing stretches. Make your meals healthier. Make your thoughts positive. Control what you can control!

Although some people may appear to be in total control at all times, it's probably an illusion. Don't spend time comparing yourself to others because you'll always feel like you are not as good as them. Compare your life now to what your life used to be before you started taking control of it. You will see the positive change you have made, and chances are you'll feel better.

Make things happen; don't just let them happen. If you want a better life, don't sit and wait for it to fall out of the sky. You'll be sitting for a long time. Work toward what you want. If you keep doing the same things every day and thinking about how you dislike what is happening, you will likely not change. If one day you decide to do one thing that makes you happier, that day will be a little happier. Do this enough days in a row and you'll see change.

"I don't see any results."

If you've been working hard at making changes, you are likely seeing results. They may not be the results you were expecting (maybe you didn't hit your big goals right away), but notice the progress and celebrate it. If you woke up 15 minutes earlier and read a chapter of a motivational book, celebrate that. Celebrate little things often enough and soon you'll be able to celebrate the big results.

I once had a client who was recovering from a horrible farm accident and had been confined to her home for months. Her injury did not allow her to drive. When she was finally able to, she drove a few miles. It was a big deal, so we celebrated. As time went on, she drove farther and farther. We celebrated each step along the way. Soon, she was back to driving like she did before her injury.

The first time you do anything, it's a big deal. The first time you do something better than you did before, it's a big deal. The first time you notice results happening, it's a big deal. Take the time to be happy and celebrate.

At first, you might be too wiped out to realize what you've accomplished. If a seemingly simple task takes that much out of you, it was probably a big deal. Keep telling yourself that it will get a little easier every time and be less tiring. Psyching yourself up takes more out of you than physical effort. That's okay. Any physical effort can be a big step toward improving your well-being.

If you've been working diligently and honestly can't see any results, change what you're doing because something about it is not working. You will see results if you're working on the right things.

"I get discouraged too easily."

Unfortunately, the notion of looking for little things to lift you up also works in reverse. Little things can also get you down. The trick here is to shift your mental energy to the positive. Like the song says, *Accentuate the Positive.*

It can be difficult. However, the positive thing about hard tasks is that you can get results from them. Find one thing today that went right. Maybe it was something at work. Maybe it was a call from a friend whom you haven't spoken to in a long time. Maybe you walked 10,000 steps. Focus on what is right in your life. Write down a list of all the things that went right today. Focus on adding something to the list every couple of hours.

Before you go to bed at night, take a look at the list and think about why you're glad all those things happened. Then, make plans to make tomorrow's list a little longer. The first thing on your list can even be that you made a list and worked at improving your state of mind. Go from there!

Study your list when you feel down. Reviewing all you accomplished yesterday will inspire you to accomplish things today. Challenge yourself to make a bigger list each day. Celebrate as your list gets longer. You'll find that after a while you won't even need lists. You'll be used to celebrating and seeing the positive.

"Okay, okay! I'll do it. What do I need to do?"

Setting goals helps you produce measurable results. Luckily, setting goals is not a hard-to-understand process. Let's take a look at how you can get started.

Define what you want.

The first step is to decide what you will set as your first goal. Think about something you want to accomplish to improve yourself but haven't **yet** been able to achieve. Brainstorm in an area of your life where you would like to see some improvement. Think about the steps you will need to take to improve. Write all your ideas down and slowly refine the process until you have a specific, measurable, time-bound goal you feel good about.

Remember, the most important thing you can do is write everything down. You want to be able to remind yourself what you are working for and how you plan to achieve the final result. You need to be able to review it, tweak it, refine it and measure it until you realize the level of success you are working to achieve.

Decide how you will achieve it.

To get closer to your dream, decide what steps you will need to get there. What does your end goal look like? What must you do to achieve it? Are there several small steps or can you accomplish the goal all at once? What day will you set to celebrate? How will you celebrate? How will you know when you've met your goal? You need to answer these questions so you know what you are working to achieve. Again, write it down!

Break down the steps.

Write down what you will have to do to reach every step of your goal. Commit to specific steps every day, every week, every month. Write down each step you will take. Remember to share them with people around you who will support what you are trying to accomplish. Post your goal in an area that will allow you to review your steps every day. This will remind you what you need to do to achieve it.

If you write your goal and never review it, you will likely never achieve it. Post it in multiple places like the bathroom mirror, on the refrigerator door or on a former junk food cabinet. Use them to remind yourself what you are working to accomplish.

Stick with it.

This is the most obvious step, but it can also be the hardest. Make your plans so you work on your goal a little every day and don't get discouraged. Remember, Rome wasn't built in a day. I am sure they reviewed their plans thousands of times and made changes along the way. The results mattered more than the process. The most important thing is to keep working and moving forward.

Celebrate!

Reward yourself once you've met your goal. Be proud of what you've done.

Congratulate yourself!

You've set and achieved your first goal. Tell people what you have done. Let them celebrate with you. Hearing their positive words will motivate you to set and achieve your next goal. My husband and I do routine household chores. At times, we point out what we did so the other is aware. We say things like, "I don't know if you noticed, but…," and "Did you see that I…." It may sound silly to you, but making each other aware of what we did gives us the ability to congratulate the doer on what was accomplished. Secondly, it feels good to celebrate each other's work.

Repeat.

There are always new goals to set and achieve. Keep setting goals and you'll find your achievements getting bigger and bigger. Goal setting will be easier. You'll feel proud of accomplishments and you'll have tangible rewards to enjoy. You'll be hooked on setting goals and finding new levels of success!

Service to Others

When I came up with the NATS acronym for my fitness regimen, it wasn't just because it works with my name. I truly believe that Nutrition, Aerobics (Activity), Mind training and Service are equally important parts of a healthy lifestyle. The service component sometimes gets questions: *Why do I have to serve others in order to meet my goals? Don't I already have enough to do?*

I would challenge you to look at all the people and resources you may have leaned on to reach your goals. You most likely did not accomplish them by yourself. There is strength in numbers and people helping each other.

I would challenge you to look at all the needs in your community. Now that you are working on yourself and finding success, you're more in control of your life. You've figured out how to live a healthy lifestyle. One healthy person is great for the community. Imagine how healthy the community could be if you help other people around you get healthy. You'll be multiplying the benefits you've already gained.

Obviously, service to others will benefit other people. What can be harder to see is that servicing others can help you. You'll see yourself reflected in the faces of each person you help. You may see that you have advantages others don't, which will cause you to be even more grateful. By helping someone else, you'll get an additional sense of pride for doing something you didn't have to.

Many people in society don't value serving others. Don't be one of those people. You've been given so many gifts in life. Share those gifts without taking anything away from yourself.

"What does service have to do with fitness?"

Serving others won't help you lose weight, build muscle or burn calories, but it will help your health. Serving others will help you see all you've accomplished and all you've been given. Helping others will put the positive and negative aspects of your life in perspective. It will make you more grateful for what you have.

My wish for you is that you work with people who need help. Assisting them with everyday tasks (eating or getting out of bed) will make you more appreciative of what you can do on your own. You can eat the foods you want or get out of bed whenever you want without help from someone else. As an added bonus, it should inspire you to take care of yourself so you can be active when you get older.

Find something you want to do that will make you feel better and make our world a better place. Work with kids, families, battered women, homeless people or those recovering from addiction. Work with people who need to know that somebody cares and has their back when times are rough.

Even if serving your community does absolutely nothing for you (which I doubt very much), it will help others on their journey through life. You can help others even if it seems like they don't need anything. They can still benefit from spending time with you. It feels good to know that someone cares. As you read earlier in this book, mental health is as important as any other aspect of taking care of yourself. Helping others can help get you in a better mental space.

"I don't have time."

It's great if you have a whole day each week to spend helping others, but it's also great if you can spare even a small portion of your day. It doesn't take long to write a thank you note, pick up trash in your neighborhood or call someone who needs cheering up. Helping someone else is easy. It doesn't have to be a grandiose event. Little things make a difference, too. Think about the best thing someone has done for you lately. Was it as simple as smiling at you or teaching you a new skill? Do that for someone else and see how it makes you feel to make a difference in someone else's life.

Be creative. You can help others while you go about your day. When you're at the grocery store, pick up a few extra non-perishables for the food shelf. When you take your kids to the park (or anywhere), see if there are a few neighborhood kids who would like to go with you. When you go for a walk after dinner, see if the local animal shelter has any pets that need to be walked. When you make dinner, freeze an extra pan and take it to a struggling family. When you run errands on a cold winter day, check to see if you can pick up anything for a shut-in.

It does take a little effort to help people, but it doesn't have to be a big deal or a chore. It may be inconvenient, but it can really make a difference to someone else. It doesn't take a lot of time and it doesn't need to break your routine. Use the time you have and work with it. Build it into your plan and write it down so you are committed to it. If you only think about doing it, you will be more likely to blow it off. If you write it down, you will be more likely to follow through. It will mean so much to the people you help.

"I don't know how to help."

People who need help live in every community. Look around and see who might be hurting. Look in the newspaper and see who had a recent death or birth of a child. Could they use some form of support that you are capable of providing? Is there someone in your neighborhood who could use some comfort or a *Thinking of You* card?

Look out your window. Is there someone in your neighborhood who could use some help getting groceries or mowing their lawn or shoveling snow? Is there a group at your children's school that needs adult supervision or needs a book read to them? Is there a nursing home in your area where you could read the newspaper to the residents? Maybe there's a single mom who needs someone to watch her kids for a few hours so she can have some time to herself.

If you're great at sewing, think of someone who needs a

costume made or some clothes mended. If you're handy at building things or fixing things, find something that needs to be built or fixed. Teach a class about your hobby. If you're great with people, rally the troops for a fundraising event. If you love organizing, help schedule events or get volunteers for a non-profit. Maybe there's a theater that needs volunteer ushers for their next production.

You can even find a way to help people by doing something you've been dreading. Clean out your closet and donate clothes to someone who needs them. Get your car washed at a charity car wash. Have a garage sale and donate the money to an organization in your area.

Use your skills and talents to do something for those who don't have your skills. You will be grateful for your skill set and they will be thankful for your help. Use whatever you're good at to help someone else.

If you can't think of a way to help others, make a list of activities you love doing. List all the ways you could use those skills to help others. Offer support for a non-profit that needs your skills. Look online, at a donation list or on a community bulletin board, then call them. I guarantee they'll find a way to use you, or at least refer you somewhere else.

Look around for someone who needs support and see what you can do for them. There are many people who just need a little something to help them through this life. Find a way. You can do it.

"I can't handle that much reality."

Let's be honest. Some people don't do anything for others

because they don't want to be around those who need help. It's a lot easier to stay in your comfort zone with people who have everything you have. It's easy to avoid things you don't want to do. However, as an adult you realize it's usually not a good idea to avoid what needs to be done. Staying in your comfort zone doesn't allow you to grow. Don't use fear of the unknown as an excuse for not helping others or improving yourself. Be careful not to put yourself in a dangerous situation, though. You need to go about helping others wisely.

If fear is a reason for avoiding service, try something a little more behind the scenes. Stuff some envelopes, use the computer to make a program or flier, crunch some numbers and put them in a spreadsheet. There are plenty of ways to help organizations away from the front line.

Take some time to learn about organizations in your community. Learn about the people they help. Observe what the front-line workers or volunteers do. Maybe you can meet some of the people they help. Learn why the organization exists and what they've done to help others. Ask how many people depend on this group's work.

Fully engage in what you're doing. If you feel inspired, you may eventually find the reality of the situation is not that scary. It's okay to jump in and work directly with the people who need your support most.

You get to know more about people when you help them. You may find out you have more in common than you thought. Maybe they can help you with something. If someone shares his/her story with you, it might inspire you to do something different in your life. It can be as simple as putting a smile on your face.

"I need too much help, myself."

Finding someone to help is almost as easy as finding some-one who can help you. Figure out what you need and what you're willing to do to get help. Look around for a person or a group that can help you. Ask people you know if they have any ideas. They may be able to help you or know some-one who can. Many communities have hotlines that make references to non-profit organizations. There's no shame in getting the help you need. If you're specific about your needs, you're likely to find someone who can help.

You could work with people who have the same problem you are struggling with (or have struggled with). I worked with people suffering from eating disorders while I was recovering from my own. I was better able to understand what they were going through and why they were doing it. I was able to pass on coping strategies I had learned. They were more likely to listen to me as the voice of experience. Many support groups have former members helping at their meetings.

A word of caution: Make sure you have dealt with your issues before you immerse yourself in other people's similar issues. When I was dealing with my eating problem, I spoke with other girls in my position about ways to hide what we did and how to get by on less food. We thought we were giv-ing each other good advice, but the tips we were giving each other would have kept us sick. If doctors hadn't been there to make sure we were learning healthy habits, no one would have recovered.

The voice of somebody else's wisdom can be the voice of

someone who gives bad advice. That could cause you to get in deeper trouble with your issues.

If you're too deep down in your issues to actively reach out to help other people, be sure to appreciate the people who are helping you. They are giving time and energy to help you get better. You don't have to fall over yourself, but a simple *thank you* or a hand-written note would mean a lot to them. You're acknowledging them for helping you, and your encouragement may be just what they need to continue helping others. Helping people solve their issues can be stressful and thankless. Professionals burn out and leave the field, leaving fewer people to help those who really need it.

When you're in a more stable place, remember all the help you were given and pay it forward. Share your great knowledge and stories of struggle with others. You will have much more credibility and you will be a provider of hope because they will see that you overcame your issues. So can they.

"There's too much corruption. I can't beat it."

It seems like every time you turn around you hear about someone embezzling money or doing bad things. Professionals are abusing clients, coaches are molesting athletes, and people are charging money for services they never provided. The actions of these wrong-doers affect the non-profit sectors. People who help others aren't necessarily better than those around them.

Sadly, people will always do things you don't agree with. The good news is that you can do well, knowing your contribution is making a difference in someone else's life. You can make a difference by not abusing your power or position. You can be the person who isn't corrupt or who leads others away from doing wrong. Leading by example is the best form of leadership.

The best way to be confident in your work is to know who you're working with. Do some research before you get involved with a cause or organization. Learn who's in charge and what their personal and business values are. Learn about the people you'll be helping and what kind of support they will need so you'll know how to help them. You'll never know for sure if you can trust someone, but this should not stop you from making an informed decision. You can't let fear of what other people will do or say control your life. Don't let it stop you from doing good in your community.

"I wasn't raised to help others."

My parents raised me to help others. They set an example for me by donating to the church and other organizations that supported human needs. They were not afraid to pitch in where they were needed. They always did their deeds quietly and never asked for recognition. They were silent leaders, never needing to blow their own horns.

My parents have carried this trait forward well into their 80s. They have made it a priority to help those in need. My mom delivered for Meals on Wheels, even though she was old enough to have meals brought to her. My dad volunteered on several community groups and served his church board. During one meeting, he had a mild heart attack. He didn't realize he was in trouble until he mentioned how he felt to others in the meeting. They made him go to the hospital immediately. This saved his life and gave us more years to enjoy him.

If he hadn't been doing his good deeds around other people, he may not have survived. Maybe you've made an impact in some way that may have saved someone.

My parents are retired now, but they haven't stopped helping others who are less fortunate. They have been able to contribute throughout their lives. Over the years, people have informed me how my mom or dad helped them through their troubles over the years. My parents are living proof that doing good for others benefited them. You can do the same thing!

One of my friends called me one day and asked if I would help build a house for Habitat for Humanity. I was super busy during that period and didn't really have time to spare, but I said yes. It was so rewarding to help the homeowner realize the dream of owning a home. My efforts made someone else's dream come true.

That was a powerful feeling and one I will never forget. I worked on that project with some of my good friends. We have great memories and share laughter when we recall our time building that house.

It may seem unreasonable at the time to give up your Saturday to mow someone's lawn or clean up graffiti, but fight the urge to say no. Try helping those around you. It may feel so good you'll want to do it again.

"I won't get anything out of it."

Maybe you won't get direct benefits from serving the community, but you will get a sense of satisfaction. Here are some other things you can gain by helping others:

Increased skills

Helping others may allow you to practice something you want to learn more about. For example, if you'd like to be handier around the house, do some volunteer work for Habitat for Humanity. If you want to work on your computer skills, offer to do a newsletter or design a fundraising brochure. If you're taking a class on web design, create a web page for a non-profit. If you're already good at something, use your time helping others to get even better.

Networking

When you help others, you'll meet people with similar interests. You may find you have the same passion as other people you spend time with. You'll see how much you have in common with your fellow volunteers and the people you serve. You never know where that next referral or best friend will come from.

Résumé building

Similar to a skill-building advantage, you can use the volunteer opportunities you've done to help yourself find a new job. Include examples of your volunteer work in your résumé cover letter. If you have permission, you may even use the organization's director or supervisor as a reference. Some community groups even give certificates or awards to those who volunteer. If you are lucky enough to be acknowledged in this way, you can list it with your achievements. Employers love people who give back to their community.

Giving your brain a workout

Do something totally different than what you do at your 9-to-5 job. If you have an office job, do something outdoors. If you spend the entire day on your feet, work with computers at an organization. If you're cooped up in an office with no one to talk to, work with people on a project. Build your leadership skills by chairing a committee.

Volunteering gives you an opportunity to try new things which will help you learn new skills. When I worked for Habitat, I did not know how to hang siding. Later in life, when my husband and I bought a fixer upper, I was able to help him re-side our new house. He loved the help and I enjoyed sharing my new found skill.

**"My family takes up too much time
for me to help others."**

Your children will do whatever they see you do. Community service is no different. They'll see your community service and want to join in. Take them to meet the people you're helping. Show them where you go and what you do. Tell them about all the good things you're getting from your volunteer work and let them know they can make a difference, too. Take them along on projects where they can help. Children can sort clothes, wash cars, serve meals or sit and talk to someone who just needs to be heard. Think about how happy you are when you see children spreading joy to others.

When my children were young, they delivered presents

to shut-ins at nursing homes. They were amazed at how the elderly were so excited to see a young person delivering a present to them. They still talk about this at some of our family holiday gatherings.

Taking your kids to help may give them skills they'll need as they grow up. They'll understand what it means when they make fun of someone for being different. They'll see that the world is bigger than them. They will see that not everyone has the same advantages as them.

Even if your family doesn't include children or others who want to join you in your volunteer work, you can still benefit your family and yourself. Think about the people you're helping and working with and all the good you are doing. They'll be thankful you took some time to help them. They'll think you're a great person and will love spending time with you, especially if it benefits them in some way or another.

Working together teaches children the value of helping others. You are planting the seeds for the next generation of helpers. Families grow stronger when they learn to lean on each other. You can lead your family to do better by the world. Go out and try it.

"I'm not confident in myself. I can't help others."

Nothing will boost your confidence faster than helping someone. Showing your skills is a great way to remind yourself of what you are able to do and what you do well. You're a part of something bigger than yourself and you're contributing to a better world. That's quite an accomplishment for one person.

I've mentioned that volunteering is a great way to make new friends who share the same interests. Being obliged to meet and work with others will give you confidence. You will feel like a contributor and will feel good about being able to support those around you. You'll need to overcome the initial fear of being around others to get started. Think of all you can gain by helping. Why wouldn't you do it?

Confidence doesn't come from being perfect or from doing something exemplary. There are many people in this world who have the odds against them and still find ways to help others. They rise above circumstances to be happy and confident.

Think about what holds you back. See how others around you are conquering their fears and building their confidence levels. Be inspired to knock down your barriers and build your path to help out. Write a goal and make an action plan for accomplishing it. You can track your progress and celebrate your success when you accomplish your goal.

"I'm only one person. I can't make a difference."

If everyone thought and acted that way, nothing would get done and the world would be the same place it's always been. All it takes is someone who is willing to do a little more. A bunch of little somethings added together is progress. Be that someone.

Earlier, I mentioned you should work on goals in small incremental steps. It's the easiest way to conquer a big problem. The same is true when helping others. You may not be able to solve the whole problem or situation, but you can do your part. There are many organizations and causes that need support. I would challenge you to find one and offer your time, talents and support.

Worried about the condition of teenagers? Work with an after-school program to help kids learn positive ways to spend their time. Think the environment is in trouble? Clean up a beach or ditch near your house. If you worry about the economy and how there are too many people without jobs, work with a group that helps people train for and find jobs. You may not be able to solve a huge world issue, but you can help with a local problem. You can't do everything, but you can do something. You can do more than you think.

Recall the last time something big happened in our country or in your community. It is likely that people banded together to make donations of clothes, money or whatever was needed. People gave blood, prayed for people who were affected and opened their homes to people who lost everything.

You can do that. If there's a family in your area with a sick child, take the other children to the park during their medical appointment to give the parents a break. If there's a park or another area in your community that needs supervision, organize a group of parents to take shifts covering it. Drive a veteran to a doctor's appointment, help at a food shelf, make a pan of your favorite goodies and deliver them to a shut-in neighbor. Every day, the news tells us about all the ugliness happening in our world. It is our responsibility to do something that brings sunshine. As one person, you can make a difference.

"There's no reason to be nice."

In this modern world where people are too busy to say "Excuse me," or "Bless you," it's easy to forget how important those common courtesies really are. Hold a door open for the person behind you when their hands are full. Help unload a grocery cart for a mom with screaming kids. Smile at someone. It doesn't have to take all day or be a big deal. Your small gesture might be the nicest thing someone has done for them lately.

I cannot tell you how many times my clients tell me that some little phrase or comment I made to them changed their lives. You have likely seen or heard about people who were about to end their lives until a sudden interaction changed their mind. Small bits of kindness can change the world.

There's no reason not to be nice. As long as you're out in the world and living your life, you may as well brighten someone else's day with a nice gesture. It might just be the one thing that makes the difference to someone who needs it.

"Natalie, smiling at someone isn't going to make a difference."

Smiling is just as easy as not smiling, and it'll make a bigger difference in the world. If all you can bring yourself to do for others is smile at them, do that. Going about your day and doing little things for others does make a difference.

You have probably heard that smiling takes less energy than frowning. Research shows that people who smile feel happier and appear more approachable to those around them. They have also found that people tend to mirror the facial expressions of those around them. When you smile, it is likely those around you will smile. Give it a try and see if the research is right.

"What about other people's contributions?"

The only person you can control is you. There's no guarantee that other people will pitch in and do their part in any given situation. You do your part, and hopefully it will inspire someone else to do theirs.

A great way to encourage people to help others is to acknowledge and thank them when they do something. Let them know you appreciate their efforts. It's a good way to encourage people to continue contributing to others.

Those around you are more likely to get involved if you are actively involved. Try to lead by example. Invite those around you to join in and thank them if they do. Better yet, send them a *Thank You* card in the mail. Everyone needs a mailbox brightener. That little act of kindness might be the catalyst they need to get involved in something bigger the next time something needs to be done.

"I'm too shy."

The best way to meet others and come out of your shell is to come out of your house. Work with people who want to change the world the same way you do. You may have to reach out to friends. Reaching out to others can have many benefits.

If you are shy, start slowly. Spend a little time helping a few people. Working with a small group can be less intimidating than working with a large group. Get a group of your friends to go with you for support. A familiar face will make your new environment seem more friendly. If you can't get your friends to join you, use this time to grow your skill set.

Introduce yourself to someone in the room who looks approachable (look for a smile). Take a few minutes to get to know that person. If you are uncomfortable with this idea, work to get to know one of the people you're helping. Someone in the group may be just as shy as you and may need a friend.

If you're shy, find a cause that needs support which can be done from the comfort of your home. There are causes that need people to sew blankets, make quilts, pack boxes of food, etc. Reach out and offer to help. Don't let shyness stop you from making a difference.

"I write checks."

In addition to physical help, there are also people who need financial donations. It's great if you are in a position to give money. Your cash donation may be just what is needed to allow an organization to keep its doors open. Many organizations depend on financial donations to continue helping others. If you can write a check or donate money, keep doing it.

I would like to challenge you to also get physically involved. If everyone were to write checks, there'd be no one else to do actual work. People and organizations would not be able to continue to do their work efficiently.

Your time is valuable, but consider rolling up your

sleeves and getting in the trenches. You're doing a good deed with your monetary donation, but take it one step further and lend a hand.

**"Okay, okay! I will get involved,
but I don't know what to do."**

It's easy to get started doing good work for people. There are many ways to make a difference. Exactly what you do will be as unique as you are. You have a talent, a skill set or knowledge base that is unique to you which can improve someone else's life. You just have to think about where and how you can share your talents.

If you are ready to get involved…

1. Decide who you want to help. Think about your passions and how you can use those to serve other people. Think about a cause you are passionate about and want to provide support to. Think about something that troubles you when you see it in the news or hear about it at a community event. Spend time thinking about how you can use your talents to make it better.

2. Find a group or an organization with the same passion as you. Contact them and offer your services. Work with them to make a plan for your involvement. Pick a time to get started. Then commit to doing it.

3. Share your passion with others you know. Try to get them to join you. Working with a friend makes volunteering more fun. Finding someone to join you in your volunteering efforts may make a difference in their world.

That's it... for now!

As you finish this book, I hope you were able to reflect on each situation while asking yourself how it could relate to something you have faced in your life or may be challenged with right now.

In the past, your excuses may have stopped you from taking advantage of opportunities you may never get back, but that's why it is called the past! You have a future in front of you that's full of opportunities to improve your life and those around you. Don't let your excuses stand in the way of growing and finding success in areas where you could be thriving.

You are stronger and more capable than you think you are. It is my hope that I motivated you to improve your overall life, health, eating habits, exercise habits and service habits. It is my desire to help you live HAPPIER, HEALTHIER, LEANIER and STRONGER!

Connect with the Author

I'm a positive speaker and dedicated to finding easy, effective exercise solutions to get bodies in shape. There are no gimmicks in what I teach! If you want to achieve a healthy lifestyle, it takes smart work, dedication and a willingness to learn about yourself and your health habits. I have helped thousands of clients achieve their personal health and life-balance goals.

Let me help you or your organization!

Natalie's Website and Email link: